A Shell Gu

𝔑𝔬𝔱𝔱𝔦𝔫𝔤𝔥𝔞𝔪𝔰𝔥𝔦𝔯𝔢

TO
FRIENDS, NEIGHBOURS AND COUSINS
IN NOTTINGHAMSHIRE
haud immemor

A Shell Guide

Nottinghamshire

by Henry Thorold

Faber and Faber 3 Queen Square London

First published in 1984
by Faber and Faber Limited
3 Queen Square London WC1N 3AU
Printed in Great Britain by
BAS Printers Limited
Over Wallop, Stockbridge, Hampshire

© Copyright Shell UK Ltd 1984

Although sponsoring this book,
Shell UK Ltd would
point out that the author is
expressing his own views.

British Library Cataloguing in Publication Data

Thorold, Henry
A Shell guide to Nottinghamshire.
1. Nottinghamshire—Description and
travel—Guide-books
I. Title
914.2 '204858   DA670.N9

ISBN 0-571-13390-8
ISBN 0-571-13391-6 Pbk

Acknowledgements

My first debt of gratitude must be to Mr John Piper, CH, Editor of the *Shell Guides*, for asking me to write yet another volume in the series. 'There are a few counties still unallotted,' he said to me in 1977, when I was writing *County Durham*, 'What would you like to do?' I asked if I could do *Nottinghamshire*. 'Of course,' he replied; 'I don't think anybody else wants to do it.' Nottinghamshire is indeed another unappreciated county. Great gratitude to him. And great gratitude to Mr Edward Piper for his beautiful photographs, and his brilliant design for the book—and to Mr Peter Burton, who once again produced box after box of magnificent photographs.

Nottinghamshire became for me the 'promised land': it has amply fulfilled its promise. I am grateful to many friends throughout the county for their help and hospitality: to them the book is dedicated. I must mention especially Mr and Mrs Richard Beaumont, Mr Myles Thoroton Hildyard, the Venerable David Leaning, Archdeacon of Newark, Mr and Mrs William Packe, Mr David Rowbotham, Mr and Mrs Andrew Skirving, Mr and Mrs Edmund Staunton, and Mr Keith Train. Mr John Barratt (with Tigger), Mr John Stevens-Guille and the Revd Basil Wilks (with his camera) were frequent companions on expeditions; Sir Jasper More once again helped with railway history. I am also grateful to Commander Philip Francklin, RN (formerly Lord Lieutenant of Nottinghamshire), Mr Eric Freckingham, the Revd Gerard Irvine, Mr E.C.A. Sheppard, the Revd George Thomson—for his constant hospitality to the Bentley—and to the Provost and Chapter of Southwell Minster, where I so often worship.

As I write these lines, news comes of the death of Sir John Betjeman, founder of the *Shell Guides*. It was those earliest spiral-backed volumes which thrilled me in the 1930s; it was he who invited me to write my first *Shell Guide* in 1960. My final tribute—of gratitude and affection—must be to him.

Henry Thorold
Marston Hall, Grantham
May 1984

List of illustrations

Note: Captions to the photographs include place names in **bold type**. These refer to entries in the gazetteer, pages 34–188.

Fourteenth-century fragments . . .

Fledborough

△ Sugar beet factory and Newark spire from **Kelham**

The Trent

◁ At Hazelford Ferry, **Bleasby**   ▽ **Kelham** silhouette

Introduction

Nottinghamshire is wonderfully unknown, blissfully undiscovered among English counties. 'How are you getting on with your book on Northamptonshire?' more than one friend has asked me during the past four years. Northamptonshire is indeed well known and dear to me; but it is not Nottinghamshire. The special quality of Nottinghamshire is that it is unknown and undiscovered—a county of scarred but ancient beauty, of unpretentious character, and unselfconscious charm.

It is the county of Sherwood Forest and the River Trent, of power stations and coal-mines, of unfrequented country lanes and dull suburban roads, of handsome towns and ghastly industrial settlements, of ducal estates and housing estates, of Royalists and Round-heads, of the Midland Railway and the M1, of county cricket and Stilton cheese, of Player's cigarettes and Boots Pure Drug Company, of terrible subtopia and glorious empty countryside. It is the county of Robin Hood and Admiral Lord Howe, of Archbishop Cranmer and Dr Robert Thoroton, of Lord Byron and D. H. Lawrence, of Nicholas Hawksmoor and Hodgson Fowler, of Paul Sandby and Richard Parkes Bonington. It can boast its own University, and one of the best of all English Cathedrals.

From earliest times the great Forest of Sherwood (the Shire Wood) occupied the heart of the county: it stretched from Nottingham in the south to Worksop in the north, and in its lonely territories sprang up the great monastic houses of Welbeck and Rufford, Worksop, Newstead and Blyth; the Norman kings hunted in it, and a royal palace was built at Clipstone. It is still the heart of the county. Overtaken by collieries and industry, by suburban and urban growth, tamed by the motor car, polluted by smoke and sulphur, strewn with the tins, paper and beer bottles of the populace, the great forest still survives. Stand in the church-yard at Blidworth and look south, or on the high ground near Kneesall and look west, walk up the back lane from Rufford towards Wellow and look north—the Forest lies before you, for all the presence of a village near by, a colliery on the horizon; there are ferns and birches, groves of gnarled and ancient oaks, plantations of more recent larch and pine. Look at the map: Kirkby Forest, Budby Forest, Rufford Forest, Clipstone Forest; Forest Farm, Forest Lodge, Forest Town; Robin Hood's Hills, Robin Hood's Larder; Thieves' Wood, Parliament Oak, Pilgrim Oak, Greendale Oak, Major Oak; Mansfield Woodhouse, Holbeck Wood-house, Norwell Woodhouse—evocative, romantic names. The great parks of the Dukeries, and of Newstead and Rufford, were enclosed from the Forest: these are sanctuaries indeed. And then there is the ghost of Robin Hood: 'legendary outlaw' proclaims the *Dictionary of National Biography*, 'his historical authenticity is ill supported'. Yet his portrait appears on local buses, his statue by the gatehouse of Nottingham Castle, he appears in literature from the early 15th century; he is supposed to have married Maid Marian in Edwinstowe Church, and to have died on 18 November 1247; he may have been the Earl of Huntingdon. Mythical or not, Robin Hood is the great hero of Nottinghamshire.

Near **Fiskerton**

How to see Nottinghamshire

Nottinghamshire is a county of remarkably varied scenery: a trip to the far south will take us to the gentle undulating country of the wolds—a land of unexpected views across to Leicestershire and the heights of Charnwood Forest, with villages of unexpected charm: Kingston-on-Soar, Normanton-on-Soar, Ratcliffe-on-Soar (with its Sacheverell tombs); Willoughby-on-the-Wolds (with the early Willoughby tombs), Sutton Bonington, Rempstone, Wysall. The scenery is delectable.

An expedition to the western frontier will take us to the Erewash Valley, to lands scarred by industry—to Eastwood and Awsworth, to Hucknall and Selston, to Kirkby-in-Ashfield and Sutton-in-Ashfield, to Skegby and Warsop. It is D. H. Lawrence country—scarred countryside indeed; yet

even here are unexpected treasures: Strelley, Cossal, Beauvale, Teversal, Sookholme.

The far north of the county is like a strip of the West Riding, which has mysteriously strayed into Nottinghamshire, scarred countryside indeed. A sortie to these unknown lands will take us to mining villages of raw red brick—to Shireoaks and North Carlton, Langold and Harworth; yet even here there are wonderful things to see: Worksop Priory, the Saxon tower of Carlton-in-Lindrick, Blyth Priory; and the village of Blyth is one of the prettiest in the county. The open countryside is never far away, and the landscape has a bracing north country character.

The scenery of central Nottinghamshire is better known: 'The Dukeries' is a term, coined in the 18th century, for the four ducal estates of Welbeck, Worksop, Clumber and Thoresby; Nottinghamshire was

◁   Towards **Bothamsall** (*top*) and looking south over **Rempstone**.

Thoresby

pre-eminent for its dukes—Norfolk, Portland, Newcastle, Kingston. All four estates marched with each other, all four rivalled each other, and all four noble owners were descended from Bess of Hardwick (of course). Clumber now belongs to the National Trust; Welbeck and Thoresby still belong to their ancestral families; Worksop has passed into other (private) hands. It is thanks to these great, enlightened and 'improving' families that so much of Sherwood Forest still survives. Clumber Park is always open: Bodley's Church, the ghost of the demolished house, give the place a powerful atmosphere; Rufford—with the crumbling remains of its great house—is open too, sad and supremely beautiful; Thoresby, with its great Victorian house, still privately inhabited, is sometimes open. Here is an incredible patrician conglomeration to be found nowhere else in England. Yet here again the scenery is scarred: the mining village of New Ollerton, the great colliery at Edwinstowe, mining sprawl at New Clipstone and Forest Town, press hard upon the celebrated Major Oak, the mouldering ruins of King John's Hunting

Palace. But a tour of the Dukeries is delightful and rewarding.

The unsophisticated charms of the Vale of Belvoir—as yet unscarred—are shared in part by Nottinghamshire, Leicestershire and Lincolnshire, but the lion's share belongs to Notts. A day here is pure delight: every mile or so, in all directions, is yet another unspoiled village: Staunton, Granby, Screveton, Flintham, Car Colston, Colston Bassett, Hickling, Upper Broughton, Owthorpe, Langar. The list seem interminable, and Belvoir seems never far away; there are modest churches with towers and spires, and the Grantham Canal makes its meandering, inconsequential, overgrown way through the heart of it.

There is a secret tract of countryside between Southwell in the south and Tuxford in the north, which is perhaps the most beautiful in the county, marvellously unknown: Halloughton and Halam, Hockerton and Kirklington, Upton and Ompton—these are some of the delicious rose-red villages to be found here, in this unscarred heart of the county. There is a lane

which leads to Winkburn, on to Maplebeck and Kersall, and so to Laxton—with its Open Fields; another leads from Bathley (a tiny hamlet with a procession of red-brick farms and barns) to Norwell, on to Ossington and Moorhouse, and so to Comper's church at Egmanton; the existence of these quiet wooded lanes must not be publicized: they are perfect.

Lastly, to the north-east, is a vast flat stretch of solitary country, where the Trent makes its majestic way northward, to the Humber and the sea. Beyond East Markham, the gentle hills subside; anywhere east of the Great North Road are uneventful lanes and uneventful villages: Darlton, East Drayton, Stokeham, Treswell; Laneham right on the river bank, Littleborough with its little Norman chapel close to the site of the Roman road which crossed the river here; Sturton-le-Steeple, with its enormous many-pinnacled tower like a big square birthday cake set with a dozen candles—and so to West Stockwith, where the River Idle and the Chesterfield Canal join the Trent, and a Dutchlike village with a little church of Georgian charm sits upon the bank. All this lonely riverside is dominated by three gigantic power stations—High Marnham, Cottam, West Burton: here they stand like three gargantuan pagan temples, where the smoke of the sacrifices goes up day and night. This is strange, empty countryside, where an unlimited tableland can be set against an unlimited sky, where London and the outside world seem a thousand miles away. A quiet lane along the low hills to the west, leading from Grove to Leverton, surveys the wide prospect of the river and all three power stations: the church towers of North and South Leverton and the steeple of Sturton look like dwarfs, and Leverton Windmill looks like a toy. Here a visitor will wish to spend a day.

Architecture: the Towns

Tribute has been paid to the scores of villages of unselfconscious charm which abound in Notts: rose-red cottages, rose-red farms, rose-red pantiles everywhere. Now for the towns. As we all know, Nottingham is the Queen of the Midlands—the Castle stands on one hill, St Mary's on the other, with the narrow streets of the Lace Market around, and High Pavement, Middle Pavement and Low Pavement connecting the two hills with a splendid sequence of 18th-century houses; the Market Place is vast, with the domed Council House and its booming chimes marking the passing hours; all around, notable Victorian offices and shops—and, below the Castle, that remarkable pleasance, The Park, with its many-styled Victorian houses. There are, it is true, some terrible towering recent buildings; but with its river, its tree-lined boulevards and its parks, Nottingham is a very individual city. Nottingham is south country. Worksop is a north country town; there is dreadful sprawl of raw red brick surrounding it, but the old streets in the centre still retain some fine houses of the 18th century, and the Priory is a church of great importance. Mansfield, with its steep streets and its Market Place, has been much torn about of late, with many old houses and old streets sacrificed to new 'relief' roads; but with its great railway viaduct towering over all it is a town of character. There is much to attract us at Retford: what other town of its size can boast two ancient churches? There is a Market Place of Georgian houses, with a fascinating, domineering, Victorian Town Hall, and in the streets around there are plenty of worthwhile houses. Go to Newark. Stand in the Market Place and gaze round: John Carr's Town Hall, the medieval White Hart, grand 18th-century houses standing on their stone colonnades—the

Wiverton Hall from the garden at **Langar**

great spire presiding over all. There is no more distinguished Market Place in England. Add to all this the Castle, Lady Ossington's Coffee Tavern, and many streets of Georgian houses, and we can place Newark as one of the best towns of its size anywhere.

Towns; p 18 **Newark** ▷
p 19 top **Retford**
bottom **Mansfield**

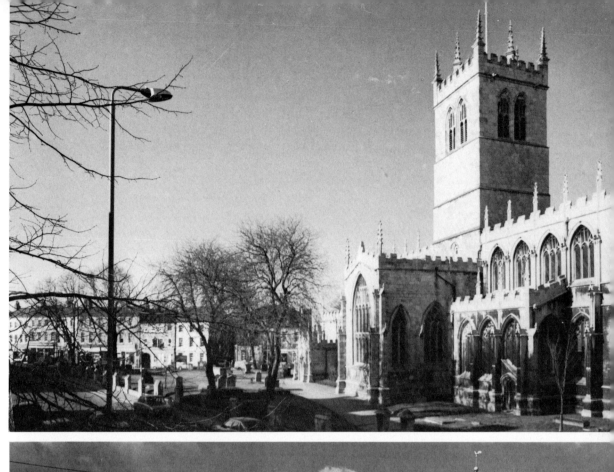

Southwell

There can be no two opinions: Southwell is one of the most enchanting little towns in England, presided over by its delectable Cathedral. It is astonishing how little known both town and cathedral are; for centuries the Minster, with its college of prebendaries, served as a kind of subsidiary cathedral, an extra 'bishopstool' in the great archdiocese of York. In 1884 the new Diocese of Southwell was formed—embracing the whole of Nottinghamshire—and Southwell became the Cathedral. Southwell has always been pre-eminent, both architecturally and spiritually: its 'Rhenish caps' are unique in England, and its Chapter House is without peer; its great legacies of prayer and music are gloriously maintained. 'At most cathedrals under the eye of a bishop,' wrote John Byng in the *Torrington Diaries* (1789), 'six o'clock prayers are left off; here they are continued, and there is regular service performed three times a day all the year round'—he commended the music and singing at the Evensong which he attended. The same is true today: Evensong is sung daily, and the standard of music has never been higher. The Diocese celebrates its centenary in 1984. The new diocese was established on 2 February and its first bishop consecrated on 1 May 1884.

Nottingham

Southwell

The Churches

As for church architecture, the county can boast superlative early work: the Saxon cross at Stapleford, the Saxon tower at Carlton-in-Lindrick, tympana at Hawksworth and Hoveringham (and several more), fragments of early carvings at Shelford and elsewhere, great Norman fonts at West Markham and Lenton—the latter one of the most notable in England. The Norman naves at Blyth and Southwell are supreme; Worksop is a little later; at South Scarle and South Collingham two village churches display important Nor-man work. There is the great Early English choir of Southwell, the Lady chapel of similar date at Worksop; the west front of Newstead, though a ruin, is comparable to Wells and Salisbury; there is elegant Early English at Thurgarton—and many a village church can show an Early English arcade of brilliant form, such as South Leverton and Rolleston. As for the Decorated period, Nottinghamshire again excels: the Chapter House, the chancel screen at Southwell; the Easter sepulchre at Hawton—indeed, the whole chancel there, with its sedilia and great east window; important Decorated work, too, is

◁ **Hawton**: the Easter sepulchre, detail △ **Southwell**: the Pulpitum, detail

to be seen in the chancels of Sibthorpe and Car Colston. There are Perpendicular churches of great magnificence at St Mary's, Nottingham, and Newark; East Markham is a grand village church of this period; Kelham is smaller, but equally distinguished. There is the rare and undisturbed medieval ensemble of Strelley and Holme-by-Newark.

Seventeenth-century work is always rare: there is the south aisle at Holme Pierrepont, and a gloriously furnished 17th-century interior at Teversal; Blidworth and East Stoke have Tuscan arcades of the early 18th century; West Sockwith is a complete early Georgian church, Ossington a polished little work of John Carr, and Papplewick, a little later, an endearing little building in Strawberry Hill Gothick. As for the great Victorian architects, Pugin built the Roman Catholic Cathedral at Nottingham; Pearson St Paul's Daybrook; Temple Moore St Mark's Mansfield; Cottingham the neo-Norman church at Thorney; Hodgson Fowler the village church at Grove; Hine the new colliery church at Shireoaks. But the greatest of the lot is without question the church at Clumber, built for the Duke of Newcastle by Bodley and Garner—supreme in every way. In the same breath may be mentioned Comper's wonderful furnishing and decoration of the little medieval church at Egmanton—a masterpiece.

Great Houses

There have been many casualties: of the greatest mansions, Smythson's Worksop was burnt down in 1761; its successor (by James Paine) was demolished in 1839. The first Thoresby went up in smoke in 1745; its successor (by John Carr) was pulled down in 1871. Nuthall Temple was destroyed in 1929, and Clumber in 1938; Rufford was abandoned just before the Second World War, and largely demolished soon after. Welbeck had its fire in 1900, and is now an army college. Wollaton survives—filled with stuffed birds and beasts; Newstead is a museum, Kelham offices, Bestwood an hotel, and Serlby is to be converted into flats. Only the Victorian Thoresby survives in private occupation.

But of the smaller houses, many survive, still owned and lived in by their rightful families. Holme Pierrepont, stripped of 19th-century stucco, has been wonderfully brought back to life by descendants of its builder; Winkburn, too, has been miraculously rescued by its ancient family, after years of dereliction. Thrumpton is splendidly cherished. Flintham has come into its own, loved and admired as it never has been before; the Stauntons are still at Staunton, as they have been since 1041. Two remarkable Smythson houses, Shireoaks, and Manor Lodge at Worksop, though much knocked about in the past few centuries, are in process of being rescued by new owners, and the rare early 18th-century garden at Shireoaks is being heroically revived. Papplewick has recently changed hands, and a rescuer is at hand for Ollerton.

Farms and Farm Buildings

And besides great houses, mention must be made of notable rural buildings. Sir Thomas Parkyns, the Wrestling Baronet of Bunny, was himself an amateur architect who in the early 18th century built the most individual of baroque houses for himself, and farms and cottages near by; Mr Acklom of Wiseton was another 18th-century amateur, whose farms and other buildings still bedeck the hills around his estate; and the two Pocklington brothers, of Winthorpe and Carlton-on-Trent, also deserve an honourable mention

Shireoaks

for their later Georgian houses in their villages, especially at Winthorpe. But all over the county the most handsome farm buildings will be seen: great barns, great quadrangles of mellow brick (or, in the north, of stone), often with dovecotes attached, or other architectural features. Hatfield Grange near Cuckney; Hodsock Grange near Langold; Corner Farm at North Leverton; Eastwood Hall—these are perhaps preeminent, but there are many others. And there are medieval dovecotes at Sibthorpe and Thoroton.

Coal and Canals

Coal has dominated the west side of the county for centuries: mines at Strelley and Cossal, Wollaton and Selston, were being worked in the 13th century; it was from his vast coal profits that Sir Francis Willoughby built his great house at Wollaton. In the 18th century the industry expanded: the Chesterfield Canal was built in 1775 to transport coal to the Trent at West Stockwith; two years later the Erewash Canal was formed, from Sawley near Long Eaton, to joint the

Manor Lodge, **Worksop** ▷

Bevercotes
Calverton

Blidworth △
Warsop Vale ▽

Cromford Canal in Derbyshire; the Nottingham Canal, from Cromford to Nottingham, followed in 1789, and the Grantham Canal in 1793. So coal from Notts could be carried in all directions.

Railways

A still more momentous event occurred in 1832, when at a meeting at the Sun Inn at Eastwood the coal owners of the district resolved to establish a railway to transport their coal. The Midland Counties Railway was born, and the first train from Nottingham to Derby ran in 1839; the Midland Railway itself came into being in 1844, when the Midland Counties, the North Midland and the Birmingham and Derby Junction Railway were united, and a regular service all over England was soon established. The line from Nottingham to Newark was opened in 1846, and charming little Tudor (or cottage *ornée*) stations were built—such as that at Fiskerton. There is also a handsome station, in the Jacobean style, at Worksop (1850) on what was the Manchester, Sheffield and Lincolnshire Railway.

Celebrities

It remains to mention some of the distinguished men and women who were either born in the county, or were closely connected with it. Thomas Cranmer (1489–1566), Archbishop of Canterbury, was born at Aslockton; Robert Thoroton (1623–78), antiquary, was born at Screveton; Thomas Smith (1631–99), banker, was born at Nottingham; Francis Willoughby (1635–72), naturalist and traveller, was born at Wollaton; Nicholas Hawksmoor (1661–1736), architect, was born at Ragnall; Lady Mary Wortley Montagu (1689–1762), who introduced the practice of inoculation, was born at Thoresby; Thomas Pelham-Holles, 1st Duke of Newcastle (1693–1768), statesman, was not born in the county, but belonged to a family intimately connected with it; Thomas Sandby (1721–98), architect, and his brother Paul (1725–1809), painter, were born at Nottingham; Richard, 1st Earl Howe (1726–99), admiral, was born at Langar; William Henry Cavendish-Bentinck, 3rd Duke of Portland (1738–1809), Prime Minister, was born at Welbeck; Charles Manners-Sutton, 1st Viscount Canterbury (1780–1845), Speaker of the House of Commons, was born at Averham; Henry Kirk White (1785–1806), poet, was born at Wilford; George Gordon, 6th Lord Byron (1788–1824), poet, was born in London, but lived for many years in Nottinghamshire, where he is buried; John Evelyn Denison, 1st Viscount Ossington (1800–73), Speaker of the House of Commons, was born at Ossington; Richard Parkes Bonington (1801–28), painter, was born at Arnold; William Booth (1829–1912), founder of the Salvation Army, was born at Nottingham; Samuel Butler (1835–1902), philosophical writer, was born at Langar; Hodgson Fowler (1848–1910), architect, was born at Rolleston; Jesse Boot, 1st Lord Trent (1850–1931), founder of Boots and philanthropist, was born at Nottingham; Edmund Henry, 1st Viscount Allenby (1861–1936), Field Marshal, was born at Southwell; Sir William Nicholson (1872–1949), painter, was born at Newark; David Herbert Lawrence (1885–1930), novelist, was born at Eastwood; and Sir Donald Wolfit (1902–68), actor manager, was born at Newark.

Nottinghamshire—county of scarred but ancient beauty, too little known, too little loved: it is a pleasure for one whose family has for many centuries lived close to its border, close to the Three Shire Bush, to pay this tribute of admiration and affection.

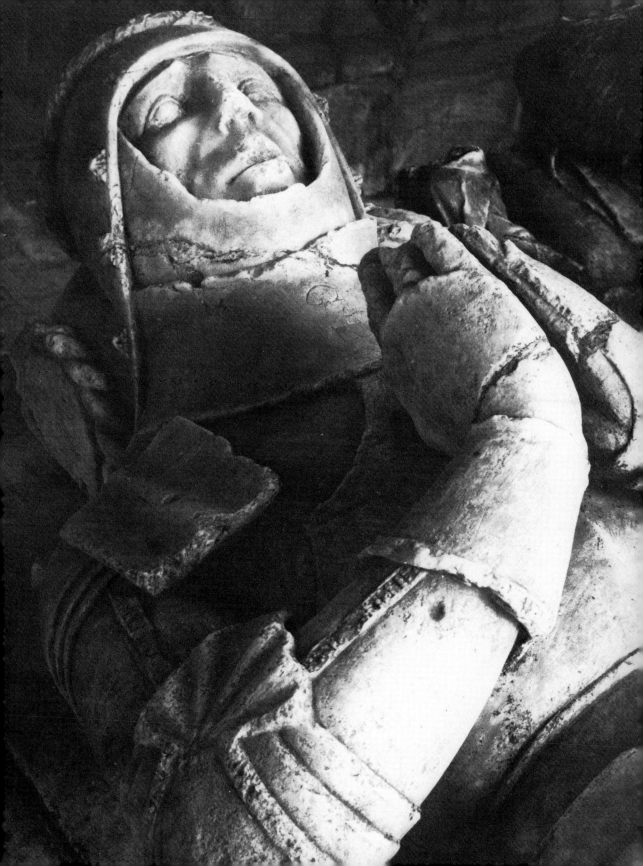

△ **Staythorpe**

The Power Stations

High Marnham, from **Clifton**
West Burton, from **Saundby** ▷

▽ **High Marnham**

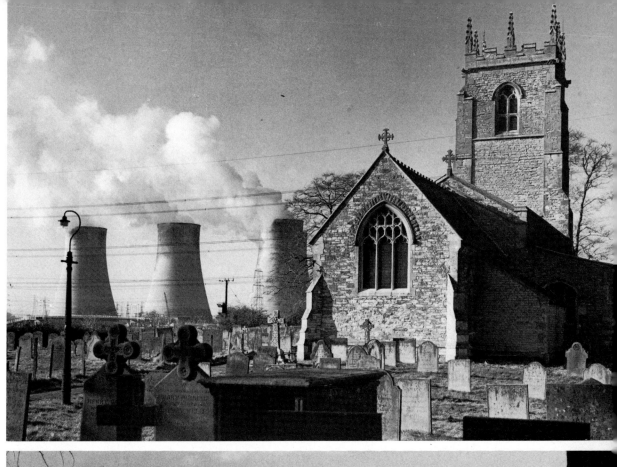

Gazetteer

Buildings or sites of particular interest are shown in italic.
The number in brackets following the place name refers to the square on the map at the back of the book where the place is to be found.

Annesley [10] A solitary gatepier above the road on the northbound carriageway of the A611 (Nottingham–Mansfield) proclaims the proximity of a great house, but to find the house and the old church it is necessary to go on and turn left along the A608: here, surrounded by trees and shrubberies is the ruin of the ancient church, abandoned when the new church was built close to the mining village in 1874. It is still possible to discern a few Dec and Perp features of this sad, roofless ruin: many of its fittings have been transferred to the new church. And near by stands Annesley Hall, for three centuries the principal seat of the Chaworths and Chaworth-Musters. A gatehouse and stable range lead into the forecourt, which incorporates the medieval home of the Annesleys: the Chaworths of Wiverton (*see* Langar) married the heiress here in the 16th century. Much of this rambling, gabled house is late 17th century, but 18th- and 19th-century work is also prominent; on the W side there is a long terraced garden with 17th-century balustrades. The family have recently abandoned the house for Felley Priory, a smaller, ancient house on the estate—a 17th-century gabled front, incorporating Tudor and earlier work, and the remains of an Augustinian priory, overlooks a walled garden and a wooded valley beyond. Annesley is to be converted for other purposes. The mining village is to the N, and on a grand hilltop site, with dramatic views to the colliery in the valley below, stands the new *Church* by Sir T. G. Jackson. The spire is a prominent landmark; the interior is lofty and spacious, and contains many objects from the old church: a Norman font, a 14th-century female effigy, a 16th-century shrouded male figure, and a small brass of 1595 to William Breton, a forester, with his bow and arrows and faithful dog. There is a great plaster achievement (1686) of the arms of Patricius Chaworth (3rd Viscount Chaworth) which formerly decorated the tower arch of the old church. From Colwick (Nottingham, q.v.), where the church is also a ruin, come many Musters monuments: of special interest is that to Sir John Musters, a London merchant who bought Colwick in 1648, 'according to Mr Camden descended from the ancient family of de Monasteriis of Yorkshire'; there is also the window, copied by Sophia Musters from the Reynolds window of the Virtues in New College Chapel. It is a remarkable magpie collection. (The earlier Chaworth monuments are at Langar.)

Arnold, *see* Nottingham

Askham [8] A remote spot in the by-roads of NE Notts: traffic roars past along the Great North Road to the W, along the main road from Dunham Bridge to Markham Moor to the S, and the high-speed trains cut across a corner of the parish; but the quiet village street climbs its modest hill, the church on one side, the *Duke William* on the other. 'Eventide brings all home' reads the inscription on the lychgate: the church has a tall pinnacled Perp tower, an earlier aisleless nave (with Norman masonry) and chancel, roofed with red tiles; decorative niche at chancel arch; 17th-century altar rails.

Aslockton [14] Venerated as the birthplace of Archbishop Cranmer. The Cranmers were a family of country squires, and Thomas was born here in 1489; only the ancient motte, called Cranmer's Mound, survives to recall the manor house which stood near by. Here, it is said, he would sit when young, and listen to the bells of Whatton (q.v.) pealing across the meadows. The little late Victorian church (1890 by Sir Reginald Blomfield) was built when the population grew with the coming of the railway: it is not unattractive and stands in a beautifully planted churchyard. The *Cranmer Arms* keeps the family name alive here.

Attenborough [13] The approach from the main road (Nottingham–Long Eaton) is terrible: subtopia, suburbia, industry. But down the side lane there are relics of the old village, and the church stands near the river, where gravel workings have provided great lakes: a short distance to the W the Erewash flows into the Trent. The church has a tall 14th-century spire, lofty nave with lofty arcades, long chancel. The plain 13th-century piers were 'improved' with entertaining animal heads on the capitals in the 14th; the excellent chancel stalls (by C. G. Hare) have early 17th-century panels inserted, carved with mermaids and mermen and the initials 'I.P.' denoting a member of the local recusant family of Powtrell, and there are two tall medieval stall ends on either side of the chancel door. On either side of the E window there are corbels for statues of saints, near by a carved and painted shield of the Powtrell family; in the S aisle the elegant

marble monument to Emma, wife of William Charlton of Chilwell (1814), also the Charlton hatchment; and in the N aisle the monument and hatchment of Admiral Sir John Borlase Warren of Stapleford; ancient S door with early ornamental ironwork. Ireton House, at the W end of the church, was the birthplace of Henry Ireton, important Parliamentary commander, and Cromwell's son-in-law. The lane called The Strand leads on to the river, and to a great *nature reserve* established here in 1966 among the lakes and islands along the river. It is a pleasure to stand here and watch the ducks, and survey the wide view upstream with Ratcliffe-on-Soar power station dominating the horizon.

Averham [11] (pronounced Aram) Close to the banks of the Trent— the overbearing presence of Staythorpe power station close at hand. The village street leads down to the *Robin Hood Theatre*, the former rectory, and the church. The theatre, founded in the rectory stables in 1913 by the Revd Cyril Walker, Rector of Averham, still flourishes: here Donald Wolfit, a native of Balderton (q.v.), first performed. The Old Rectory is a late Georgian stuccoed house, with sash windows and the Sutton arms over the front door; a path at the side leads to the *Church*. A delectable position: old trees, old headstones, a wooden calvary, the river below: views across to Newark, upstream to Rolleston and downstream to Kelham; great yews and cedars behind shield the tomb of Robert Chaplin (1837), rector, and prebendary of Southwell. Much early Norman herringbone masonry in the tower and the body of the church; Perp porch and tower buttresses adorned with the arms of the Suttons, and an impressive interior, with spacious, aisleless nave, spacious chancel—the nave pewed and panelled by Hodgson Fowler, in memory of Joseph Walker (1907), father of the founder of the theatre.

The chancel roof is gaily painted; there are tombs of the early Suttons in the nave, a grand tomb to Sir William (1611) in the sanctuary, and, opposite, a monument to his eldest son, the 1st Lord Lexington, so created by Charles I in recognition of his part in the defence of Newark (d.1668). There is ancient glass in the chancel, assembled by the Revd F. H. Sutton of Brant Broughton (Lincs); there are iron candelabra by Coldron (of Brant Broughton), a few old stalls, and ancient screen. At the W end the carved capitals of the tower arch (heads and beasts), the panels of continental glass, and the Chaplin-Sutton hatchments complete a memorable interior. No trace remains of the Suttons' great house, destroyed in the Civil War; Kelham (q.v.) became their principal seat. But on the hills to the W, in a romantic, isolated position, stands *Averham Park House*, a hunting lodge, built by the 2nd Lord Lexington in the earliest years of the 18th century. The house is of brick and was originally crowned with a balustraded top and cupola; attendant wings enclosed the entrance front on the W side. Balustrade and cupola and N wing have disappeared, but the rooms contain painted panels and over-doors by Jacques Parmentier, and the central vista through the house commands a view of Newark, aligned on the spire, commemorating the defence of the town by the builder's father. Two contemporary paintings show the house as it was then: in one it stands on its hill-top, rather like Ashdown Park, the hunting lodge built by Lord Craven on the top of the Berkshire Downs; the other shows the entrance front, with deer standing outside the white gates. The front door stands open, and through the open door beyond, Newark spire appears, glistening in the sunlight.

Awsworth [10] The Erewash Valley, the M1, the dual carriageway of the A610—somewhere in this tri-angle is Awsworth: main road housing, main road shopping, main road traffic. There was an 18th-century church here, built for Mr Smedley, a coal owner, but the nave was rebuilt in rather ordinary Edwardian Gothic in 1902, the chancel more recently. The *Bennerley Viaduct* crosses the Erewash here—an iron lattice bridge of 16 spans, built in 1887 to carry the Great Northern line from Nottingham (Victoria) to Derby (Friargate). The line is closed, but efforts are being made to preserve the bridge.

Babworth [5] The *woods and plantations of Babworth Hall* accompany the Worksop road (A620) as it leaves Retford: there is no 'village'—only a lodge or two, the white-painted stuccoed former rectory, with its late Georgian bow window and early Victorian gabled dormers, and the church half hidden in the trees behind. Babworth was acquired by William Simpson from the Elwes family (of Saundby) at the end of the 17th century, and remained in their possession until the end of the 19th. The Hon John Bridgeman Simpson, younger son of the 1st Lord Bradford (of Weston, Staffs) succeeded his uncle and assumed the name of Simpson in 1768; it was he who employed Humphry Repton to transform the house and its surroundings between 1795 and 1820, and his 'Red Book' survives, setting out his schemes. The early 18th-century red-brick house was stuccoed and whitened, the park landscaped, and the lake formed. He married a Worsley of Appuldurcombe; his son Henry succeeded him and a younger son William became rector of the parish; his daughter Henrietta married the 1st Earl of Yarborough and as heiress to her uncle, Sir Richard Worsley, brought Appuldurcombe to that family. Later in the 19th century William Burn restored the red brick and added the parapet to the house; after a brief interlude the Whitaker family came to Babworth in 1898, and it is now the home of Sir James Whitaker, 3rd Bt. The house, reduced in size since the Second World War, stands in a good position surveying Repton's landscape. The *Church* is Perp, with low tower and square-headed windows, and embattled throughout; there are several 18th- and early 19th-century tablets to the Simpsons in the chancel, but only the base of the most important monument survives—above the Simpson vault in the vestry: it commemorates Henrietta, wife of John Bridgeman Simpson, herself an artist, and is signed 'Repton desigt, Coade sculpt'. Above the sill of the window small figures of cherubs, one with artist's palette and easel, one with a harp and an urn, supported a framed panel of glass by Eginton of the Resurrection—lit by the window behind. All this was swept away in a 'restoration': a tragic loss. It was the only known instance of collaboration between these three artists. There is also a monument to Morgan Vane (1789) of Bilby Hall, a house long demolished which stood on the far side of the Great North Road. And in the church-yard, at the E end of the church, a headstone by Sir Ninian Comper marks the grave of Arthur James Mason of Morton Hall (*see* Ranby), Master of Pembroke and Lady Margaret Professor of Divinity at Cambridge (d.1927). Babworth has close links with America through Richard Clyfton, Rector 1586–1604, who became pastor of the Separatist church at Scrooby (q.v.), and died in Amsterdam in 1616, a founder of the Pilgrim Movement. The lane to the W towards Barnby Moor crosses the Chesterfield Canal, with its pretty lodge, and makes for Botany Bay Farm.

Balderton [12] The main road (former A1) into Newark is lined with bleak Victorian terrace houses—rather a sombre entry into the beautiful town; the village street turns off E at the traffic lights.

But there are few buildings here to notice, apart from the *Church*. This well repays a visit for its 14th-century crocketed spire, set on a tower of which the base is 13th century; for its nave arcades of the 13th and 14th centuries; for its 13th-century chancel with its lancet windows; but above all for the Norman doorway of the N porch, so splendidly carved with beakheads. Inside, there are no less than 45 15th-century benchends, with rabbits, or dogs, crouching on the finials; the pulpit and screen are 15th century also. Several windows in the chancel are filled with fragments of medieval glass, and in the sanctuary are two monuments to the Sikes family of Newark: that to Mary Sikes (1828) is signed by D.W. Willson of London—according to Rupert Gunnis, one of his two best monuments anywhere. Royal Arms of Elizabeth II, 1977. Almost in Newark itself, just short of the railway bridge, a plaque on a semi-detached gabled house records the birth here of Sir Donald Wolfit, in 1902.

Barnby-in-the-Willows [12]
Delectable: incredibly cut off from the outside world. *Barnby* can only be approached by the long lane which is the continuation of Barnby Gate in Newark, or by another lane (easily missed) off the A17, close to the Lincolnshire frontier. The River Witham cuts off Barnby from Lincolnshire on the E and S: there are only views across the river to Fenton and Claypole, whose spires pierce the sky. There are quiet lanes of old brick cottages, and an ancient squat stone dovecot. The *Church*, with its typical Nottinghamshire Perp tower (extraordinary how these are never found in Lincolnshire) is one of great charm: box pews surround the aisles, each one provided with a little shelf for prayer book and hymnal; the nave is furnished with a great array of 15th-century pews with poppyheads (some most entertaining), very similar to those at Fenton;

there are old seats in the choir; the sanctuary is furnished with Jacobean panelling, and there are bold 17th-century altar rails. Monuments to the Sharpe family: ledger stones in the chancel floor; slate tablets on the walls—one to George who died in 1686, aged 26, as Student of the Middle Temple, and another to Thomas who died in 1702 aged 19, as an undergraduate at Merton; on a marble plinth there is a bust of Mary who died in 1742 aged 24; a long-forgotten family. In the chancel, too, are windows with the most extraordinary tracery; learned authorities have ascribed them to the reign of Edward I, but they must surely be the work of some local 17th- or even 18th-century mason. They are amusing and unique. Barnby Manor, 'a large neat residence' according to White's *Directory* (1853), erected in 1848, stands close to the main road surrounded by Victorian plantations.

Barnby Moor [5]
Now by-passed by the Great North Road; celebrated for the *Old Bell*, an 18th-century (or earlier) hostelry, which still provides good food, delightfully furnished sitting-rooms, and roaring fires in winter. 'A gentleman-like, comfortable house', wrote an 18th-century traveller.

Barnstone [14]
Cement works—usually considered a disfigurement to the Vale; the village is consequently ignored or dismissed. But there are cottages and farmhouses of warm red brick, and a pretty little Victorian stone *Church* with bellcote and twirligig W window.

Barton-in-Fabis [13]
Or Barton-in-the-Beans. Sir Osbert Sitwell has described in *Tales my Father Taught Me* (Hutchinson, 1962) a pilgrimage made with his father and brother to the three Sacheverell villages of Ratcliffe-on-Soar, Barton-in-Fabis and Morley (Derbyshire)—a pilgrimage to the tombs of their Sacheverell ancestors: 'The three

days', he writes, 'were a series of triumphant anti-climaxes. It rained all the time ... At one place we visited the house had just been pulled down, and there only remained a square red-brick pigeoncote—a building which still bore the arms of the Sacheverells ...' This was Barton; but his memory deluded him: it is an unusual octagonal dovecote, and clearly visible, surrounded by farm buildings, close to the site of the Hall. But the *Church* is redolent of the Sacheverells, and the Sitwells also. On either side of the altar are their tombs: William (d.1616) and his wife with their alabaster effigies on the N side; Rafe (d.1605) with a gaily heraldic tomb on the S; Henry (d.1598) has a smaller heraldic monument near by. On the W wall of the chancel another tablet commemorates Henry Sitwell 'third son of Francis Sitwell, Esqre, and Katharine his wife, eldest daughter of Henry Sacheverell, Esqre'; he died in 1691. Thus the Sitwells inherited from the Sacheverells. On the N wall of the chancel is a marble monument to a former rector 'that honest and good man, Joseph Milner, M.A.', who died in 1750, and his widow 'this marble table caused to be erected, first bathing it with a flood of tears'; the whole inscription is worth reading. The church itself is a distinguished 14th-century building, with lofty hall-type nave (with S aisle), long chancel, W tower and spire, and 17th-century porch: pulpit (17th century) and screen (16th century) are partly restored with later carvings; there are 18th- and 19th-century Swithland slate tablets near the door. Barton is a charming sequestered village between the A648 and the Trent: brick cottages, and a long brick wall which once surrounded the home of the Sacheverells.

Basford, *see* Nottingham

Beauvale [10]
A green valley, secluded, secret—for all the proximity of Eastwood, the colliery, and

the M1. The *Carthusian house* here was founded by Nicholas de Cantilupe in 1343—one of only nine Charterhouses in England. A farmhouse, built out of the stone of the priory, occupies part of the site, and against it are the remains of the church, its walls supported from collapse by wooden buttresses. Attached to this is what is left of a tower house (the prior's lodging), and it is possible to make out the line of the cloisters, round which were built the individual houses of the monks, each with its own garden. Protected by surrounding woodlands, resplendent with golden colours in autumn, it is still possible to imagine the seclusion and peace of the place: only the distant hum of the M1, which passes in a cutting near by, infringes on its peace today. On the other side of the lane stands Manor Farm, a 17th-century house of stone and brick, with a timbered gatehouse behind; and at the other end of the valley, buried in deep woods, stands *Beauvale House*, built in 1871 by E.W. Godwin, for the 7th Earl Cowper, who had inherited the property from his grandmother Lady Palmerston, and desired a small estate house here; his main seat was at Panshanger in Hertfordshire. With its tiles, timbering and tower it is a romantic house for a romantic setting: the tower may be seen rising above the surrounding woods. (Beauvale is private property, and the Priory may be visited only by permission, which may usually be obtained at the farmhouse.) At Moorgreen, the hamlet on the road to Greasley, Godwin built a number of estate cottages; farther N *Moorgreen Reservoir* is a a great lake, adding further romance to the landscape.

Beckingham [6] On the way to northernmost Notts: the village is now by-passed, but a little Georgian *gazebo* stands in the village street, from which no doubt the inhabitants of the Hall would watch the passing traffic; a modest

mid-Victorian house now keeps it company. The *Church* with characteristic Notts tower is Perp outside, but displays EE arcades within; a somewhat Victorianized interior, thanks to Ewan Christian's restoration in 1892.

Beeston, *see* Nottingham

Besthorpe [9] A village of old brick cottages, just off the Newark–Gainsborough road—with a little brick Gothic *Church* of 1844 standing on the green. Its entrance, placed oddly in the middle of its N side, leads into a charming little interior: the altar in an apsidal sanctuary, a brick cross adorning the wall above the pulpit, a pair of marbled classical pillars at the W end, supporting the bellcote. The building cost £400, which was raised by subscription: it is ignored by all other guidebooks—let the *Shell Guide* sing its praises! Opposite stands an old Methodist chapel of russet brick, with pantiled roof and sash windows, looking like a Georgian house, and indeed attached to one. The lane W leads down to Besthorpe Wharf: not much business here now—but delightful views up- and downstream, and across to the tall spire of Carlton-on-Trent opposite. Gravel pits near by.

Bestwood, *see* Nottingham

Bevercotes [8] The great new colliery—the most modern in Notts (1964)—is a commanding feature of the landscape. Almost under its shadow, and deep in its own wooded grounds watered by the River Maun, is *Lound Hall*, rebuilt in 1937 by Brierley and Rutherford of York for Sir Harald Peake, now an NCB 'training centre', and the *National Museum of Mining*—open to the public regularly, and containing many fascinating exhibits.

Bilborough, *see* Nottingham

Bilsthorpe [8] Pretty, undulating countryside along the road from

Newark to Mansfield: a lane leads N to Bilsthorpe, and the sudden sight of the chimney and winding towers of Bilsthorpe colliery, peering over the low hill, is an unexpected apparition. The large new colliery village extends N: on a low hill to the E rectory, manor farm, and church comprise the old village. The *Church* tower has a top of 1663; the rest is late 14th century. Dark interior; the S chapel (by T.C. Hine, 1873) is the mausoleum of the Saviles of Rufford. Under the tower is a monument to William Chappell, Bishop of Cork and Ross, who died here in 1649, and had lived as guest of the rector during the Civil War.

Bingham [14] The old part of the village—or small market town—is attractive: the market place, the older houses and cottages there, and in the adjoining streets, the Chesterfield Arms, and the church, of course. But so much of the rest is terrible: row upon row, street upon street, of small, smug, suburban houses, stretching in all directions across the flat landscape, each with its garage, or double garage; the dreary shopping precincts, the multiple shops—which impinge upon the market place; indeed the house at the SW corner, important in the composition of the square, has been pulled down in order to make a car park; the whole thing is eloquent of the standardized, mass-produced, characterless, anonymous 20th century at its worst. Poor Bingham! The *Church* has a distinguished, sturdy, 13th-century broach spire; the interior is dark with much (attractive) Victorian glass. Spacious nave and transepts of the early 14th century; the chancel is dominated by elaborate reredos and choir stalls by W. D. Caroe—the former somewhat dull owing to complete lack of colour. Here the Victorian glass, by Mrs Miles (wife of Canon Miles), is attractive, with its grisaille pattern enlivened by medallions; there is a window in the

Besthorpe

S transept by their son Frank Miles, the Victorian portrait painter; there is another by A.R. Mowbray, then aged 24, a native of Bingham, and founder of the firm of A.R. Mowbray & Co., the church furnishers. The Market Cross (by Hine, 1861) is in memory of John Hassall of Shelford, Lord Chesterfield's agent.

Bleasby [11] The road from the railway station to the village is lined with farms, cottages, and Victorian and later villas: the railway (opened in 1849) has provided easy access to Nottingham, but the setting is entirely rural. The *Church* stands in a pretty churchyard, shaded by a great cedar; it was restored in the 19th century by Ewan Christian and others, but is in origin 13th century: with its Victorian glass and rows of pews, the interior is pious and respectable in a Victorian way; there are memorials to the Kelham family who lived at the Hall, and a handsome organ in a late Georgian case.

Opposite is the gate to the *Hall*, with its pretty facade of sash windows and battlements and Gothick corner turrets—behind the stucco much older than its 18th-century front suggests. The Old House is of stone, and in origin an early 16th-century hall house; in the 18th century the hall was divided, and an upper floor inserted. A road leads down to the Trent: at Hazelford Ferry is the *Star and Garter Hotel*, an attractive Victorian riverside hostelry, standing by itself on the river bank; there are grassy walks along the river, with splendid views up- and downstream, and across to the tree-hung hills opposite.

Blidworth [11] (pronounced Blid'th) 'Sherwood Forest' announces a notice on the roadside, approaching from the E: there are some plantations of conifers, a 1960s public house called the *Jolly Friar*, and the road dives into Blidworth, to an enormous estate of 1930s miners' cottages. These are,

in fact, rather good—though in some cases barbarous modern windows have destroyed the proportions and ruined the design. Approaching from the N, from Rainworth, there is a fine view of Blidworth colliery; the roads meet at a grand baroquish 1920s public house, called the *Forest Folk*. There are more miners' houses, some shops, and the road to the W leads up to the old village on the hill; here there are more public houses, old stone cottages, and the church. From the churchyard there is a grand view to the S, over what indeed was Sherwood Forest, somewhat mutilated now by coal-mines and human habitation, but still well wooded and curiously remote. The *Church* is one of great charm: a building of 1739, little altered, with a Tuscan S arcade, round-headed windows, W gallery with organ, flat ceiling; there is a curious font, of 16th- or 17th-century date, with Perp tracery on one side, a cherub's head on another, and bold lettering 'Romans

VI 3 & 4' on a third; Jacobean panelling in the sanctuary, and a late Georgian Gothick pulpit from Southwell; there is continental enamelled glass of richest hue, and a rare 18th-century psalm board, with King David painted on its reverse; the whole church is exceptionally well furnished, and has a compelling devotional atmosphere. There are a number of interesting monuments: one, to Thomas Leake, Ranger of the Forest, killed there in 1598, is a small alabaster tablet with a touching rhyming inscription, and surrounded by carvings of stags and dogs and the emblems of his office; and in the sanctuary are several tablets to the Need family of Fountain Dale (a house in a charming situation near Rainworth Water), recalling their military prowess; all these are worth reading.

Blyth [5] The great Perp tower of the *Priory Church* dominates the village, dominates the landscape. It is a tower of great beauty with lacelike traceried parapet connecting the eight tall pinnacles. From up the churchyard path, the building appears at first glance all Gothic, with its Dec porch, embattled S aisle and large Dec windows. Only at a second glance do the small Norman windows of the clerestory give a clue of what is to come. The door opens: at first the attention is caught by the exceptionally wide S aisle, all furnished and set out as though this were the church, with high altar, organ, pulpit, pews. Suddenly there is a glimpse of the great Norman nave beyond—which opens out miraculously: a great arcade of the utmost severity, a triforium of stark simplicity, the small windows of the clerestory and the very early quadripartite vault above. It is breathtaking. The Priory was founded in 1088 by Roger de Busli as a cell of the Abbey of St Cuthbert at Rouen: the nave must have been begun at the very end of the 11th century. It is French in character, primitive, solemn, al-

most grim—but of rocklike beauty. At the end of the 13th century the S aisle was rebuilt to serve as the parish church—as indeed it still does. There are seats in the nave, but no altar, only the blank E wall dividing what was the parochial nave from the monastic church beyond. At the Dissolution, central tower, transepts and choir were destroyed: what survives was claimed by the inhabitants as their church. The Norman N aisle is narrow and mysterious, dark with richly coloured Victorian glass. And there is much to see in the church: medieval screens, with painted panels of saints, early sepulchral slabs, an early Purbeck marble effigy of a knight, a 17th-century font with cover, 17th-century pulpit, and many hatchments of the Mellish family. In the Lady chapel is an imposing monument to Edward Mellish, whose bewigged figure reclines between Corinthian columns (1703); it is by John Hancock. 'It was extremely difficult', writes Rupert Gunnis, 'to find Hancock's signature ... indeed I was only able to discover it by climbing a ladder, for it was tucked away at the top of the right hand pilaster supporting the carved pediment.' It was Edward Mellish who built Blyth Hall, which stood to the W of the church; it was a distinguished, late 17th-century house (perhaps by Talman)—'a very sweet house and gardens and grounds', wrote Celia Fiennes, 'it stands high and commands the sight of the country about'. Unfortunately a later member of the family, at Brooks's or Carlton House, gambled Blyth away—and the family retired to Hodsock Priory near by, where their descendants still live. The village owes much to the family: Edward Mellish's grandson, William Mellish, was a great friend of John Carr—who built the *stone bridge* over the River Ryton, which still gives pleasure to travellers along the A634. There are terraces of brick cottages with Gothick windows, a handsome

stable block with central archway, and the former Rectory, close to the church, crowned with a cupola. The Hall itself fell on evil days and after standing empty for many years was pulled down in 1972. There is a smaller green near the church, and a long green accompanying the full length of the long *village street*, on either side of which are many delightful houses. At the far end is St John's Hospital, founded as a leper hospital, rebuilt, with older features, in the 15th century, and later used as a school. It is a peaceful street now, with the traffic of the A1 rushing past on the new by-pass. *Hodsock Priory* stands deep in its parkland and wooded meadows; the house (which in fact was never monastic) descended from the Cressy family to the Cliftons of Clifton (q.v.), who used it as an alternative to Clifton Hall. There is a wonderful 16th-century brick gatehouse leading to an early 19th-century Tudor house, which was added to in the 1870s by George Devey. Beautiful gardens have been formed within the ancient moat. Across its wellwooded park, and visible from the A1 on a clear day, stands *Serlby Hall*, a great rose-pink late Georgian house, three storeys high. Serlby was originally built for the 2nd Viscount Galway in the 1750s by James Paine. Pictures survive of the house as it was, a Palladian 'villa', with pavilions at either end connected by low wings: Paine made use of his familiar motif of wide interlocking pediments and a vast spread of roof. It was a composition of considerable charm and distinction—but from the practical view inconvenient. The 5th Viscount employed Lindley and Woodhead in 1812 to remodel the house: the pavilion wings were swept away, the central block enlarged and heightened, pilasters and a Tuscan porch added to the S front. From the aesthetic point of view this is perhaps disappointing —though the view from the N of the great house rising above steep grass

◁ Priory nave, **Blyth**

terraces is impressive; but grander rooms could be provided within, and very fine these are, decorated in the late Georgian Adam manner. The *Small Dining Room* survives with Paine's more sober Palladian decoration. John Monckton, 1st Viscount Galway, was grandson of Sir Philip Monckton, the distinguished Royalist; General Robert Monckton, who was second-in-command under Wolfe at the capture of Quebec and afterwards Governor of New York, was brother of the 2nd Viscount; the 8th Viscount was Governor-General of New Zealand. The *Park*, with its terraces descending to the River Ryton, is of great beauty; the estate still belongs to the family, though the house is now being converted into flats.

Bole [6] A dead-end lane off a minor road leads to the little village; a cart track leads on to Bole Ings, the watery meadows by the Trent. There is a handful of old brick cottages, a handful of new council houses, a 17th-century house called Manor Farm, with Dutch gables, and the *Church*. This has an endearing Nottinghamshire look, with pinnacled Perp exterior, and pinnacled Perp tower. Inside, earlier features appear—an octagonal Norman font (with double arcading) and some Dec windows —but it is like a Perp college chapel, without aisles. In a chancel window ledge there is a small brass to John Danby (1400), and the panels in the pulpit are 17th-century Flemish, given to the church in 1866 by Sir Charles Anderson of Lea (across the Trent in Lincs), a distinguished local antiquary. But a short distance to the S is the West Burton power station, with its eight cooling towers and two slender chimneys—an overpowering intrusion.

Bothamsall [8] The valley is watered by the River Meden and the River Maun, which coming their separate ways unite briefly, then separate again, then reunite for ever

to form the River Idle. A Newcastle estate village, with many good-looking cottages. The road twists and turns to give full advantage to the church standing above the village street: it is 1845 Perp, but of such mature design, and so well weathered, that it might pass for the real thing; only the rather pinched tower proclaims its date of birth. The architect seems unknown. There are relics of the earlier church—a 14th-century font, a small and early brass in the chancel, and a few monuments, one to John Marson (d.1809), 'a good husband, father, Christian and friend: his faithful services to three Dukes of Newcastle speak him an honest man'; there is another to Sir Charles Crawford (1821). The road to the W climbs gently to Castle Hill, a small motte and bailey in a prominent position, from which there are wide views across the rivers, to the great plantations of Clumber and Thoresby, and across the old site of *Haughton* to *Bevercotes* colliery (q.v.). Almost submerged in the new plantations is *Lound Hall*, built in 1937 for Sir Harald Peake by Brierley of York, a handsome neo-Georgian house, now a museum of mining, which is often open to the public.

Boughton [8] (pronounced Booton) The suburbia and industry of New Ollerton are near at hand, but the heart of the village is still a village—with its Victorian church, a handful of older houses, and its (former) *village school*—attractive with its pretty barge-boards. The *Church* is by James Fowler of Louth (1867)—ubiquitous in N Lincs, but a rare visitor in Notts; there is a small spire on the S side – unmistakably Fowlerian—a magnificent chimney on the N; the E window commemorates W.J. Pickin (d.1869), who was agent to the Duke of Newcastle, and founder of the school. There are some imposing farm buildings along the lane to Kirton; the pumping station (1905) makes an attractive group of build-

ings, if not on the scale of Bestwood and Papplewick.

Bradmore [14] Redolent of Sir Thomas Parkyns, the Wrestling Baronet of Bunny—landowner, classical scholar, magistrate, wrestler, amateur architect. He rebuilt the village after the great fire that devastated it in 1706. Note the handsome farmhouses, buildings and cottages that bear Sir Thomas's mark. Only the broach spire of the medieval *Church* survives, with a Victorian brick chapel attached.

Bramcote, *see* Nottingham

Bridgford, East [11] A pretty wooded lane leads up the hill to the village from Gunthorpe Bridge: there are views across the river, and several spacious Georgian houses give an air of prosperity to the place. There are smaller houses and cottages, a shop or two, at the crossroads in the middle of the village; here stands the *Church*, on one of the earliest Christian sites in Nottinghamshire, indeed built on the foundations of a cruciform Saxon church. The present chancel is early 13th century; the spacious clerestoried nave is 14th, and the tower a careful rebuilding of 1778, when the transepts were pulled down and the Georgian windows inserted in the N aisle. There has been much later restoration, most recently by C.E. Ponting (1913). There are medieval tiles in the N chapel, a monument to John Hacker (1620), with kneeling figures, near by, and a number of 18th-century monuments in the chancel; one is to Mrs Priaulx, widow of Peter Priaulx, DD, and mother of Peter Priaulx, BD, and another to the wife of Thomas Beaumont who was for many years curate (for an absentee rector), and built Bridgford Hill (1792), the finest of the houses which overlook the river. The somewhat earlier *Rectory* (1744) is next to the churh, and is charming with its veranda and sash windows. There is a good deal of recent housing towards the Foss.

Bradmore from the north-east

Bridgford, West, *see* Nottingham

Brinsley [10] The scarred
countryside of the Derbyshire
border: dreary housing along the
main road, and views of open
countryside and coal-mines. The
Church is of the Commissioners'
type, with a long barn of a nave,
and ornamental pinnacles at the W
end (à la King's Chapel); the
chancel an addition of 1877.

Brough [12] Once the important
Roman settlement of Crococolana
on the Foss Way: now but a few cottages, a small Victorian church,
and a still smaller Methodist
chapel, with the traffic rushing by
between Newark and Lincoln. The
little red-brick *Church* (1885) has
an exceptionally well-furnished
interior: a bronze tablet by Sir
George Frampton commemorates
the founder, Thomas Smith Wooll-
ey 'who served this hamlet for

thirty eight years' (1914), the little
lancet windows are filled with
attractive glass depicting various
saints—and General Gordon—and
a lofty iron screen adorned with
candles protects a sanctuary of
great beauty. A tiny wayside shrine
of great charm.

Broughton, Upper [14] Nether
Broughton is in Leicestershire, Upper Broughton is in Notts; a little
tributary of the infant River Smite,
running through the valley to the
E, forms the frontier. The main
road from Melton Mowbray to
Nottingham twists and turns,
ascends and descends through the
village; but the best approach is by
the gated road from Hickling,
which climbs through undulating
meadows up to the village. From
the *churchyard* there are wide ex-
hilarating views across the Vale of
Belvoir, the *Church* with low nave,
squat tower and loftier chancel

perched delightfully on a shelf of the
wolds, the Victorian Gothic rectory
on a lower shelf to the E. S.S.
Teulon rebuilt the chancel in 1855;
the nave is 13th century, the arcade
and tower 14th, and there are Norman and later medieval fragments
built into the 18th-century S porch.
The best thing of all is the array of
early 18th-century slate headstones
with raised inscriptions and decorations in the churchyard—a very
fine display. There are many agree-
able red-brick cottages and larger
houses, and the village green is
bright with daffodils in spring; behind the *Golden Fleece* is an 18th-
century Baptist chapel.

Budby [8] The main road from Ollerton to Sheffield (A614) turns,
and comes unexpectedly to Budby,
a little estate village built in the
early 19th century by William
Wilkins (junior) for the 1st Earl
Manvers of Thoresby. The river

HONESTE AUDAX

ARTIFICIS STATUS IPSE FUIT

Quem modo, travisti longo in Certamine Tempus
Hic Recubat Britonum Clarus in Orbe Pugil
iam primum stratus, praeter Te Vicerat omnes
De Te etiam Victor quando Resurgit erit

Tempus edax rerum

That Time at LENGTH did throw him it is plain
WHO liv'd in hopes that he should RISE again

ΚΑΙΡΟΣ Ο ΠΑΝΔΑΜΑΤΩΡ

Here lieth S[r] Thomas Parkyns Bar[t] one of his Ma[jesties] Justices of y[e] Peace & quorum, Deputy Lieutenant, Col[onel] of y[e]
Nottingham & Leicester, Second Son of S[r] Tho: Parkyns Bar[t] & Anne y[e] Sole Daughter & Heiress of Tho: Cressey of B
[in] y[e] County of York, Esq[r] whose Ancestors came in with William y[e] Norman. y[e] said S[r] Tho: Parkyns Married
Elizabeth y[e] Grand Daughter & Heiress of Iohn Sampson Esq[r] Alderman & Citizen of London, with whom he had
[fe]e-farm Rent of 224-02-08-½ per Annu paid out of y[e] Mannor Borough & Park of Beverley & y[e] Waterton
[app]urtenances in that County. also y[e] fee-farm Rent of 43-16-6¼ issuing out of y[e] Mannor & Castle of Bolsover in y[e] Cou[nty]
[Co]pies of y[e] Deeds of Purchase are Enroll'd in Chancery, & in Money about 3500[l]: was Educated at West-minster
[in] Graves Inns of Court 9 years, who purchased y[e] whole Tythe of Bradmore & part of Keyworth
[out] of y[e] Tythe of Bunney, Also y[e] Mannor & Estate in Ruddington
[liv]estock, wysall, Thorpe & Willoughby

Bunny school

Meden meanders through plantations of black poplars: stuccoed cottages with Gothick windows and overhanging eaves, some with porches, some with other frills, stand around. Inside the park stands *Budby Castle* (or Castle William), built by Carr of York *c.*1790, a little toy fort of stone, with Gothick windows, battlements and turrets.

Bulcote [11] Almost swallowed up by Burton Joyce—but not quite. Its tentacles stretch out along the A612 (Nottingham to Southwell) but the hamlet of Bulcote is intact. There is an early 18th-century manor house, another attractive house or two— and up the steep bank on the opposite side of the main road a little stone *Church* of 1862, with bellcote and apse.

Bunny [14] The name is eccentric (nothing to do with rabbits: it denotes the reeds and long grass that grow around here); the village nurtured one of the most endearing and interesting 18th-century eccentrics that the county produced—Sir Thomas Parkyns, the Wrestling Baronet. The Parkyns family first came to Bunny in the 16th century: Colonel Isham

Parkyns (his mother was an Isham) was a distinguished Royalist in the Civil War; his son was created a baronet in honour of his father in 1681; the Wrestling Baronet was his son. Classical scholar (he was at Westminster and Trinity College, Cambridge), mathematician, lawyer, amateur architect, squire and benefactor of the villages of Bunny and Bradmore, he was also an accomplished and enthusiastic wrestler, encouraging the young men of Bunny to practise the art, and holding wrestling matches every year. His cottages and farmhouses here and in other villages near by proclaim his style; in the middle of the village stands his *school* (1700), a brick building with mullioned windows and handsome baroque details. *Bunny Hall* he rebuilt 20 years later: its most remarkable feature is the tall tower or belvedere at the N end, surmounting a semicircular pediment, the centre of which is adorned with a great cartouche of arms, against a lavish display of weapons and mantling. Ionic pilasters adorn the corners: tremendous buttresses support the whole composition. It is Vanbrughian in spirit. Whether Sir Thomas completed the house is uncertain; the S front is quite different, built by his grandson, who was created Lord Rancliffe (in the peerage of Ireland), gabled and stuccoed in early Jacobethan style. The 2nd Lord Rancliffe died childless in 1850, leaving the property to his mistress; it has since passed through many hands, while the baronetcy passed to a cousin who lived at Ruddington (q.v.). Burke now classifies the title as 'dormant', though heirs descending from the 2nd baronet evidently exist. A notice in *The Times* personal column some years ago, appealing for the rightful heir to come forward, seems to have passed unheeded. There is a great wall round the park: the approach to the house from the village is dramatic, through a curving drive between long 18th-century barns leading up to the tower.

Grand 14th-century *Church*, with crocketed spire, and handsome pinnacled nave and aisles. Many monuments, from the first Richard Parkyns to Mrs Forteath, the 2nd Lord Rancliffe's mistress. Most notable is the large tomb to Sir Thomas himself, showing him standing ready to wrestle—with the figure of Time and his scythe in the next compartment and Sir Thomas lying on the ground at his feet. Royal Arms of George III, 1802.

Burton Joyce [11] Endless traffic, and endless suburban villas, along the main road from Nottingham to Southwell (A612); the *Church* with its large churchyard and evergreens seems marooned. It is ancient, with 13th-century tower and spire, 13th-century nave (restored by T.H. Wyatt) and 14th-century chancel, curiously out of line with the nave; there is a wide squint from the N aisle into the oddly aligned chancel, with a good geometrical Dec window above; a 13th-century font; and a 14th-century effigy to Robert de Jorz (Joyce). But suburbia has taken over: the best thing to do is to take the by-road to the station, cross the railway line, and walk along the bank of the Trent, enjoying the grand views up- and downstream all the way to Stoke Bardolph.

Calverton [11] (pronounced Carverton) Over the hill from the salubrious village of Woodborough to the industrial village of Calverton. Framework knitting was the old industry, and there are a number of early 19th-century framework-knitters' cottages to be seen: *Windles Square* (to the E along the main street) comprises charming little cottages recently restored by the Notts Building Preservation Trust. In the other direction is the Meridian Factory and, beyond, colliery housing by G.A. Jellicoe (1937). The great colliery was opened just before the war. The *Church* is an extraordinary amalgam; much of it is Georgian: 18th-century tower, 18th-century nave, early 19th-century chancel; but there are interesting and unusual earlier fragments and carvings. Some Victorian tidying-up in 1881.

Carburton [8] A tiny hamlet between Clumber and Welbeck: the Palladian gate to Clumber (*c*.1760) stands opposite one of the 5th Duke of Portland's innumerable Tudor lodges (*c*.1870), marking the boundaries of the two ducal estates. Little Norman *Chapel*, which lost its S aisle in the 18th century: Norman S door, two little Norman windows at the E end, bellcote at the W, and on the W wall a sundial; inside, the pews are painted white, there are memorial windows to Mrs C.G.S. Foljambe (as at Wellow, Edwinstowe, Ollerton and Worksop), a tub-shaped font, a little brass to John Mazine, who held an equestrian office at Windsor (1679), and a crucifix to the memory of the Revd F.C. Day Lewis (Rector 1918–27), father of the late Poet Laureate. *Manor Farmhouse* is a late 17th-century stone house with prominent chimneys; and *Carburton Grange* a pretty late 18th-century house on the edge of the woods; otherwise there are only a few cottages, and it is hard to realize that until the early 18th century Carburton possessed important ironworks, worked for a time by the Sitwells of Renishaw.

Car Colston [11] One of the best villages of the Vale of Belvoir: a great wide *green*, unusual for Notts, with a sprinkling of cottages and larger houses set around the edge, and cattle grids to all the lanes to restrain the straying cow, the wandering sheep. *The Hall* at one end is 1838-Elizabethan, of mellow brick, built for a squarson, the Revd John Girardot; Beech Close at the other, a gracious early 18th-century house with a long row of sash windows. The *Church* is up the lane to Screveton, and has a tall narrow Perp tower with conical stone top;

Carburton

but its great glory is the chancel, higher than the nave, with great Dec windows filled with curvilinear tracery. Interesting furnishings include a Jacobean pulpit and magnificent early 18th-century altar rails with projecting centre, excellent modern iron candelabra (made by Philip Willis, the Screveton blacksmith), and monuments to the Blagg family of Brunsell Hall; of special note is the tablet to Thomas Matthew Blagg in green Cumbrian slate by Bryant Fedden of Winchcombe (1975). There is a brass plate, erected in 1905, to Dr Robert Thoroton, the renowned Notts antiquary. The great stone coffin in which he was buried stands at the W end of the nave, unoccupied: it was shockingly dug up from the churchyard in the 19th century as being 'in the way', and his bones were reburied. A stone tablet erected by Dr Thoroton on the E buttress of the S aisle commemorates members of his family: alas, it is almost indecipherable. Dr Thoroton (the first syllable of the name is pronounced as in 'thorough'), whose *Antiquities of Nottinghamshire* was published in 1677, lived at the *Old Hall*, or Morin Hall, beyond the church: a tall narrow late-Georgian farmhouse occupies the site, and incorporates a few remains of the old

Bunny

house at the back. The high brick
wall which sheltered the Doctor's
garden still surrounds it. Closer still
to Screveton stands *Brunsell Hall*, a
fascinating fragment of a 17th-
century house built by Dr Samuel
Brunsell, rector of Bingham and
Screveton, and friend of Dr
Thoroton: it subsequently passed
by marriage to the Blagg family,
who have held property in Car Colston since the 18th century. There
is a drawing room with highly decorative and elaborate 17th-
century panelling.

Carlton-in-Lindrick [5] The
country N of Worksop is
reminiscent of the West Riding: the
colliery villages along the A60 with
their raw red-brick villas could well
be in Yorkshire—indeed the frontier is not far away. Such is North
Carlton; but Carlton-in-Lindrick
(the freedmen's enclosure in the lime
wood) is an ancient village, and old
stone houses abound. At first sight
the *Church* appears all Perp, but on
approaching, the great Saxon
tower with its herringbone masonry
makes its presence felt; the Perp top
was added in the early 15th century. Much Norman work survives:
the N arcade is Norman; the S
arcade was built in imitation when
the S aisle was added in 1831;
Trans chancel arch; small Norman
windows in chancel; over the
S chancel door a Norman
tympanum, showing the sun and
the moon. There is a 15th-century
alabaster carving (Nottingham
work) over the altar in the N aisle;
fragments of medieval glass have
been pieced together in a window
in the Becket Chapel; there are two
hatchments of the Ramsden family,
and a Royal Arms of George IV. It
is a numinous interior: 'This church
is open day and night for private
prayer', states a notice near the
door 'please speak quietly and
move reverently in this holy place.'
Carlton Hall, home of the
Ramsdens since the mid 18th century, was pulled down in 1955:
some buildings survive in the park,

Carlton-in-Lindrick

and the family have migrated to Wigthorpe (S of the village), where there are two good-looking Georgian houses. *The Mill*, on the edge of the park near the church, powered by the stream that feeds the lake, is now a local museum. The *Ramsden School* (1831) has Gothick windows, and wide overhanging eaves. At North Carlton, Long Lane leads to the entrance lodge to *Wallingwells*, and an endless pot-holed drive leads on and on through woods, past several stranded bungalows, to the mansion, once the seat of the White family, baronets. A small Benedictine priory of nuns was founded here in the 11th century; after the Dissolution the place was acquired by Sir Richard Pype, Lord Mayor of London, who erected the first house here out of the monastic remains. In the 17th century it passed to the Taylor family, whose heiress married Thomas White of Tuxford (q.v.), MP for East Retford (1698); his great grandson was created a baronet in 1802. Plain early 18th-century fronts with sash windows face S and W, the E front was rebuilt in the early 19th century in a romantic Tudor style. The Whites abandoned the place after the First World War, and the mansion has been divided into several dwellings. Cars, caravans, tractors stand about, and the big stableyard is surrounded by overgrown shrubberies. There is no sign now of the great 17th-century layout of gardens, canals and avenues that once adorned the place; but overlooking the small lake an 18th-century *grotto* survives—the domed interior adorned with rocks and stones and crystals—a precious link with the great days.

Carlton-on-Trent [9] A lofty Victorian spire seen from the A1 and a glimpse of the pediment of a late Georgian house above its plantations of yews and cedars: that is most people's impression of Carlton-on-Trent. It is a pleasure to turn off the main road into the

Carlton-on-Trent

Clifton Church, N and S Clifton

quiet street: there is the long wall of the big house, a group of pretty cottages, the tall Victorian Dower House on the left, iron gates leading into the Hall forecourt on the right, and G.G. Place's tapering spire to close the vista at the end. *Carlton Hall* was built in 1765 for Joseph Pocklington, Newark banker and brother of Roger at Winthorpe (q.v.); both brothers were keen amateur architects. It is a house of white brick, with two tall canted bays on the entrance front, and a flat pedimented front facing the garden: there are lower wings to right and left, one of which contains a drawing room of considerable size and splendour, with coved ceiling and elegant plasterwork in the manner of James Wyatt or John Carr; in the garden is an ancient cedar of immense size. The property was purchased in 1832 by John Vere, London banker, and is still the home of the Vere-Laurie family; it is open to the public, by appointment. The *Dower House*, opposite, conceals an older house behind its Victorian facade, and contains a drawing room with a delicately-painted early 19th-century ceiling. The *Church* was built in 1851 for John Vere, by G.G. Place of Nottingham, and incorporates the 12th-century door of the earlier church. It is a grand church in miniature, with lofty nave and Victorian glass: there is a tablet to Florence, Viscountess Massereene and Ferrard (mother of the late squire), who died aged 105 in 1978. The quiet street leads on: there are several attractive 18th-century houses, such as the Old White Hart (now a farmhouse), with its big dining room and Venetian windows—a well-known hostelry once, when this was the Great North Road; the Forge has an enormous brick horseshoe adorning the end of the house. And another quiet lane leads down to the Trent.

Caunton [8] A village of many lanes, sheltered by the plantations of the Manor from the traffic of the A616; the Beck runs between the churchyard and the *Hole Arms*: a footbridge leads to the *Church*. A Perp tower, a Perp clerestory, older arcades in the nave, a S Chapel; an old water colour shows the chancel—before Ewan Christian's restoration (1869)—with its flat ceiling and square-headed E window. In the chancel are many monuments to the Holes: a small brass records Hugh Hole, Vicar 1567–79; Samuel Reynolds Hole, celebrated as horticulturalist and rose grower, was curate, vicar and squire from 1844 to 1887, when he became Dean of Rochester. Another brass plate on the sanctuary step records that he erected the E window (by Henry Holiday) in 1872 in memory of his parents 'who here received the Bread of Life'. It portrays the sacraments of Baptism and Holy Communion. The S Chapel contains monuments to the Bristowes of Beesthorpe, and memorial windows by Heaton, Butler and Bayne (1893) and T. Dudley Forsyth (1911). The Manor, whose high garden walls line the village street, was the home of the Holes from the 18th century until 1962: a house of various dates, it was given its long pedimented S front by Percy Houfton in the early 20th century. At the E end of the village the *Grange*, a tall square late-Georgian house, with handsome stone Doric portico, is the home of Mrs Hole: here she cultivates her charming garden. W of the village, on the far side of the main road, and set back down a long drive, is *Beesthorpe Hall*, home of the Bristowes from the 16th century until the 20th; John Bristowe was Regarder—a splendid title—of Sherwood Forest in 1543. There is Elizabethan work at the back: on the front the older gables survive, but sash windows were inserted in the 18th century, and a large drawing-room and dining-room added at either end; it is a charming house. It is now a school for handicapped children, and the estate sold off. Looking across the treeless, ploughed-up park, the house appears a little forlorn, like a lost country house in Ireland.

Clarborough [5] The busy road between Retford and Gainsborough: the church lies back against the low Wheatley Hills, and with its typically Notts pinnacled Perp tower, its aisled nave and chancel, groups well against the hillside; the interior has been made gloomy with Victorian tinted glass and pitch-pine pews, but retains its 13th- and 14th-century arcades: James Fowler of Louth was let loose here in 1874. At *Welham* (to the S) there is a late Georgian house, stuccoed and cream washed, with wide bow window facing E, and cupola-crowned stables; and there are other attractive 18th-century brick houses near by.

Clayworth [5] A winsome *village street*: all the way from the humped bridge over the Chesterfield Canal, where long boats are often tied up, right to the church, pantiled cottages and larger houses, red brick or colour washed, line the way. Interesting *Church* of many dates, many parts: a typical Notts pinnacled Perp tower, but the base is Saxon or early Norman; the nave is Perp, with no capitals to the piers; the chancel is EE; there is a rare 14th-century stone screen into St Nicholas Chapel (S side), and much Victorian decoration and stained glass. A church of many vistas and many monuments: there is the Tudor tomb to Judge Humphrey Fitzwilliam and his wife in the chancel; of some interest is the tablet (in poor condition) under the tower to the Revd William Sampson, who kept a *Rector's Book*, describing life in the parish, 1676–1701 (published 1910), and the recent tablet to General Sir Robert Laycock, Governor of Malta, of Wiseton Hall (d.1968). There are many monuments to the Ackloms, earlier owners of Wiseton (q.v.) behind the organ, and to the Otters of Royston Manor near the font. Of

Mary Acklom we are told that 'on February 5 1796 she was deprived of the use of her right side by a paralytic stroke, but having great powers of resistance and an aversion to an inactive life, by persevering application acquired the ability to write and maintain a numerous correspondence.' She was the daughter of Marmaduke Constable, of Wassand in the East Riding, and died in 1801. Of the Otter monuments, the best is to Francis (d.1813) by Westmacott: the Otters first came to Clayworth in the 17th century; Royston is a Victorianized Tudor house, with views across the Canal to the meadows of the River Idle. It is now a country club.

Clifton, North and South [9] Strange, strange country: the flat, featureless lands on either side of the Trent. The Cliftons lie on the E side, two villages of brick-built cottages and farms and, between them, in complete isolation, Clifton church. A lane leads to the river and peters out; a railway bridge crosses the river a little farther downstream, but the line is now closed. Opposite is High Marnham: the *Brownlow Arms* and the power station (an awesome presence) and from there *Clifton Church* is a prominent landmark, solitary, incomprehensible, and (of course) inaccessible. The tower is imposing—13th century below, and Perp above with its pinnacled top; the nave and chancel arch are 12th or early 13th century, but the interior is scraped. The sanctuary is resplendent with Victorian mosaics, and there are good 19th-century furnishings throughout. Great iron lychgate.

Clipstone [8] King John had the good sense to enjoy hunting in Notts: indeed Clipstone Palace, royal hunting lodge in the royal Forest of Sherwood, was one of his favourite places of residence, both before and after succeeding to the throne; he was hastening thither in 1216, when he was taken ill and

died at Newark. Driving from Edwinstowe, where the road turns S in the small village of Clipstone, the rugged and jagged walls of ancient masonry—all that remains of the royal hunting lodge—stand in a field; a Parliament was held here in 1290 by Edward I, either in the palace, or under the so-called *Parliament Oak*, the gnarled remains of which stand not far away, close to the Mansfield road. James I granted the manor of Clipstone to the Earl of Shrewsbury: it subsequently descended to the Dukes of Portland, and the 4th Duke built the *Archway Lodge*, which is visible across the fields to the N, in 1842, to terminate a ride through the Birklands to Welbeck. It was modelled on the Priory Gatehouse at Worksop, to serve as a lodge below and a schoolroom above; it is adorned with figures of Richard I, Robin Hood, Maid Marian and other heroes: the architects were Hurst and Moffatt. It is now a private house. The road leads on to New Clipstone: dominated by Clipstone colliery, the new *mining village* was laid out in the 1930s on attractive lines by Houfton and Kington. Cottage-style houses and terraces (all designed by the architects) set a new standard in colliery housing. In the centre a wide square is laid out as a recreation ground, with a charming Romanesque church (in brick) at one end, a Nonconformist chapel at the other.

Clumber [8] 'A black heath full of rabbits, having a narrow river running through it, with a small boggy close or two.' That is how an 18th-century writer described this stretch of Sherwood Forest before Clumber Park was formed. It was in 1707 that John Holles, 1st Duke of Newcastle (of the second creation), was given licence to form a park here for the Queen's use, and in 1760 that his nephew Thomas Pelham-Holles, 1st Duke of Newcastle (of the third creation), began to build a great house to replace the old Holles seat at Haughton (*see*

Haughton). The descent of the Dukedom of Newcastle is complicated (*see* Welbeck): all the great families of the Dukeries were related, all were descended from Bess of Hardwick. John Holles was descended from her through his mother; he married Lady Margaret Cavendish, daughter of the 2nd Duke of Newcastle (of the first creation), who was also a descendant of Bess, and the dukedom was re-created for him in 1694. As he had no son this second dukedom also expired (1711). Clumber and Haughton passed to his nephew Thomas Pelham-Holles, George II's Prime Minister, for whom the dukedom was again re-created in 1713. When he had no son and it became apparent that the title would again expire, he was given a second dukedom in 1756 with remainder to his nephew Henry Clinton; he could not be created Duke of Newcastle (on Tyne) for the second time, so his second dukedom was of Newcastle-under-Lyme. Henry Clinton became Henry Pelham-Clinton, and in 1768 succeeded as 2nd Duke of Newcastle-under-Lyme: it is from him that subsequent dukes descend. So it was Thomas Pelham-Holles of the two dukedoms who built the house at Clumber. He and his descendants were the creators of the park we see today, and of the buildings that still adorn it—though the great house has gone. *Clumber Park* is vast and varied: the narrow river, mentioned by the 18th-century writer, is the Poulter; having fed the lake at Welbeck, it enters Clumber near the Carburton Gate, and broadens out to form the great lake: the house stood on its northern bank, and the Stables and Chapel stand there today. The long drive from the Drayton Gate (on the A614) crosses by means of a beautiful *three-arched bridge*, and continues round to the site of the house. Another drive from the Apleyhead Gate (farther N on the A614) leads through the noble double lime avenue to the same place—as does

The Apleyhead Gate, **Clumber**

another, from Worksop, through Truman's Lodge, and yet another, from Carburton, through the Carburton Gate. And the Normanton Gate (opposite the Normanton Inn on the A614) leads to Hardwick Village, the estate village in the park close to the E end of the lake. Clumber House was begun in 1760, and the architect was Stephen Wright, a protégé of William Kent, and a dedicated Palladian. The front door, standing in a canted bay, faced W: pavilion wings crowned with pediments stood at the four corners of the central block, two framing the entrance front, two a recessed centre on the S, facing the lake. It was an attractive composition, built in the finest ashlar, restrained, unpretentious. Later dukes no doubt thought it insufficiently ducal; in the middle of the 19th century it was Italianized, and

a great balustraded garden was formed on the S, with steps descending to the lake. In 1897 it was gutted by fire, and rebuilt by Charles Barry (junior), still retaining the old plan, and incorporating the old house. The result was not happy: it was ponderous and prim, and all the charm and freshness of the Palladian house had vanished. It was demolished in 1938. The red-brick *stables* are delightful, with a domed cupola crowning a white-painted clock tower, and on the site of the house its plan has lately been laid out in paving stones. Stephen Wright is still represented by his *Doric Temple*, on the opposite bank; the bridge is also his; as are all the gateways—except one. The *Apleyhead Gate*, a triumphal arch with curving screens and lodges was the principal entrance; *Truman's Lodge* is a castellated arch with attendant

lodges, half classical, half Gothick; the *Drayton Gate* has wide Kentian piers with niches and pedimented tops; *Carburton Gate* has little pedimented lodges, purest Palladian. The *Normanton Gate* has a different provenance: the two tall piers, crowned with urns, are of *c.*1700 and came from Shireoaks (q.v.). But the great glory of Clumber is the *Chapel*, whose spire points to heaven, and beckons the visitor from every direction. There have been chapels at Clumber before, but this great church was built by the 7th Duke, the restorer of the Shrine of Our Lady of Egmanton, and benefactor of other Nottinghamshire churches. Its architect was Bodley, and it was completed in 1889. It stands upon the spreading lawns near the site of the house, and close to the lake, built of grey stone, with red stone

54

The Lime Avenue, **Clumber**

from Runcorn, a lofty nave of four bays, and a still loftier chancel of equal length; shorter transepts form the crossing, from which rises a majestic spire. The tower itself is tall: from the pinnacles, flying buttresses support an octagonal corona; the lofty spire floats above. Inside, the high vaulted nave (with blind arcades) draws the eye to the crossing and rood screen: six candles adorn its loft, and the gilded rood, with attendant figures, hangs above. Beyond stands the altar, with high dossal, six candlesticks and crucifix; richly carved choir stalls are illuminated by lamps and candelabra; a Lady chapel opens from the S transept; in the N transept is a great monument by Westmacott to the wife of the 4th Duke, which originally stood in the mausoleum at Markham Clinton. The organ, with elaborate case and gallery, adorns the N wall of the chancel. Clumber Chapel has much in common with Bodley's other great church at Hoar Cross: both possess compelling atmosphere; both were designed to bring the worshipper to his knees. And Clumber chapel does: it is used regularly by local residents, and evensong is sung on Sunday afternoons in summer, for residents and visitors. A retired priest lives in the precincts and acts as honorary chaplain. There is an unforgettable *view* of the church from Stephen Wright's bridge at any time of year, with the spire reflected in the waters of the lake. The present (9th) Duke had intended to build a new house on a different site, but the war intervened. The National Trust purchased the park in 1946. It is excellently maintained and every possible provision is made for visitors. The park is always open: bicycles may be hired, refreshments obtained at the cafe, books and National Trust merchandise bought at the shop, and an excellent dinner obtained at the restaurant.

Coddington [12] Despite the traffic on the A17, this is still an attractive village of red-brick cottages and old walls. The yellow-washed *Plough Inn* stands at the crossroads, with a lane to the *Church* behind. Squat and gabled with its low pinnacled tower, it was practically rebuilt by Bodley in 1864. The nave arcades are ancient—but the great thing is Bodley's decoration of the chancel and his furnishing throughout. The painting of the ceiling and panelling in the chancel, the choir stalls adorned with candles, the canopied settle for a sedilia, the chancel screen, the almost domestic screen by the S door—all are wonderfully original; moreover the glass, in the chancel by Morris and Burne-Jones, delicate and transparent, and the later, more colourful glass in the S aisle (1881) by Ford Madox Brown and Burne-Jones, is a very great attraction. All this is due to the benefaction of the Thorpe family of Beaconfield; there is a bronze memorial to Captain John Somerled Thorpe, MC, who was killed in the First World War. On the N side of the churchyard a Wesleyan chapel of 1805 has been ingeniously converted into a house.

Collingham, North and South [9] A long double village astride the Newark–Gainsborough road—a village of fine brick houses and smaller simple cottages, gardens, old walls and many connecting lanes. *South Collingham Church* lies to the W of the green: a tall Perp tower, clerestoried nave, long chancel—the interior notable for a richly decorated Norman N arcade, complemented by an elegant EE S arcade of clustered columns; the whole church is brought to life by a splendid rood screen by Martin Travers (1940). Monument to Francis Mering (1573) in N aisle. *North Collingham Church* is also delightful, with a low Perp tower, EE arcades in the nave, a raised Perp chancel (with distinguished S door); two monumental slabs with

Clumber

Clumber

marked 'Access Anglers Only': this is a solitary spot—no ferry plies now between Collingham and Carlton.

Colston Bassett [14] Famous for Stilton cheese: a *beautiful leafy village* in the Vale of Belvoir. An ancient Cross, rebuilt in 1831 in honour of William IV's Coronation, stands at the crossroads, the *Martins' Arms* behind it, and near by an unexpected, grand Victorian *Church* with central spire, built in 1892 by the architect A.W. Brewill for Mr Knowles, the squire, in memory of his wife and son: a most imposing building, with original and lavish details and richly furnished interior. There is a large white marble monument to Mrs Knowles, and the family pew at the back of the church has upholstered seats like a carriage. The *Hall* in its Victorianized grounds looks like a very grand house in Belgrave Square: the 19th-century stucco and Corinthian pilasters conceal a much older core, which was the home of the Royalist and Papist family of Golding, baronets extinct, subsequently of the Martins. And away from the village, isolated in the park, stand the sad ruins of the *old Church*, abandoned and unroofed in 1892. There is a Norman N arcade, blocked up in the 18th century when handsome Georgian windows were inserted, a later S arcade, and a Perp tower. It stands here, crumbling; its preservation even as a ruin is urgent and imperative.

Cossall [10] looks unpromising on the map, hemmed in by Nottingham on one side, the M1 on the other, and industry all round. In fact it is a secluded oasis, protected now as a conservation area, a pretty village on its low hill, with many old brick cottages, the Willoughby Almshouses, a large farmhouse incorporating a 17th-century fragment of the old home of the Willoughbys, and the church—'the old, little church with its small spire on a square tower', as D.H. Lawrence describes it in *The Rainbow*

effigies in low relief in N chapel (14th century), 17th century font cover, heraldic shields above the chancel arch, in origin part of the misericords, oddly placed here in a 19th-century restoration; another very well-furnished church. Opposite this church a signpost 'To the Trent' points the way down a long muddy lane: the left fork leads to Collingham Wharf ('disused' remarks the map), the right leads on and on to the river bank opposite Carlton. Gates on the way are

Burne-Jones glass at **Coddington**

where he calls it Cossethay. In the novel Cossethay was the home of the Brangwen family, and the character of William Brangwen was based on Alfred Burrows, to whose daughter Lawrence was for a time engaged; the Burrows lived at the cottage near the church, marked by a plaque. Apart from tower and spire the *Church* was rebuilt in 1842—a little building of charm; there is one old marble Willoughby tomb in the sanctuary, 19th-century Willoughby glass in the chancel, and an early 15th-century panel of St Catherine in the S aisle; 15th-century font; Victorian Royal Arms over the chancel arch. The *Almshouses* were founded by George Willoughby in 1685 and form a delectable group in the village street, with their many gables all in mellow brick, with cottage gardens in front within the walled enclosure. The Willoughbys of Cossall and Aspley were a recusant branch of the Wollaton family: 'I'm told', wrote the rector of Cossall to Archbishop Drummond at the time of the Visitation of 1764, 'that there is a room in the Hospital at Cossall where, sometimes but very seldom, a Popish Priest performs some of the offices of that religion, with great secrecy and attended only by a few Poor belonging to the Hospital.'

Costock [14] The A60 (Nottingham–Loughborough) makes its way across the wolds and roars past the village; but the lanes are quiet and unspoiled. The modest-looking medieval *Church*, with Victorian porch and bellcote, stands in a back lane; in the chancel wall outside, under a canopied recess, is the mutilated figure of a priest; and near by, higher up, the fragment of a Saxon cross. The interior charms with its great array of poppyheaded pews; some of these are ancient, the rest inspired reproductions by a Victorian rector, C.S. Millard. N aisle of 1848 by G.G. Place: in its outside wall, another canopied recess is the memorial to the rector at that time, Edward Wilson. The Manor House, a smaller, stone 16th-century gabled house; another, taller, gabled stone house of the 17th century; and several good brick houses adorn the village. Half-way to Bunny, on rising ground surveying the wide prospect to the S, stands *Highfields*: now a farmhouse, and with its roof and windows altered, it was built in 1729 by Sir Thomas Parkyns as a dower house to Bunny. Its solid baroque bulk, with its angle pilasters, proclaim the hand of that amateur architect, the wrestling baronet.

Cotgrave [14] The colliery opened in 1964: great efforts have been made to landscape the setting and plant trees in profusion to mitigate

its impact. In the village, only the new housing makes its impact; from farther afield the great winding towers are only too clearly visible. The *Church* stands in the heart of the old village, which with its wide streets is attractive and intact: a late 14th-century spire rises from a plain Nottinghamshire embattled tower; inside, the nave arcades are a century earlier, the columns of the chancel arch earlier still; there has been some Victorian restoration.

Cotham [12] The quiet lane from Staunton to Hawton, the little-used railway from Bottesford to Newark, the meandering River Devon: Cotham stands on gently rising ground, and there are wide views—as far as Belvoir on a clear day. Cotham is a mere handful of cottages and one or two good-looking farms. The little *Church* stands surrounded by stone walls across a field, as charming a sight as any in Notts—but it is derelict and by the time these words are printed it may be no more; however, efforts are now being made to preserve the little building (1983). It is heavily buttressed, and the splendid Dec or Perp windows were reset in its walls in the 18th century, when the church was reduced in size and the tower pulled down. An 18th-century porch leads into what is little more than a chapel, now given over to birds, but still containing medieval fragments and Victorian glass. The monument to Anne Warburton, wife of Robert Markham (1601) has been removed to Newark. The senior line of the Markhams had a great seat here, destroyed in the 17th century after the death of Robert Markham, 'the great waster of that house', 'a fatal unthrift and destroyer of this ancient family' remarks Thoroton. If the church is destroyed, all Cotham's past will be destroyed: a tragedy.

Cottam [6] Like a vast pagan temple on the banks of the Trent, with the smoke of the sacrifices going up

day and night, the gargantuan power station dominates everything for miles around. It is the best-looking of the Trentside power stations, with its tightly-packed phalanx of eight cooling towers, and its one mammoth chimney. It was completed in 1968. Oddly enough, human life survives beneath, and for all the ceaseless hum of the engines people still live in the village of Cottam. The tiny Norman *church* is approached by a path between immaculate cottage gardens: it comprises nave and chancel and bellcote, with a well-preserved Norman S doorway. No doubt it will survive the power station.

Cromwell [9] The traffic on the A1 roars past, very close to the village on one side; the high-speed trains roar past not far away on the other; the Trent flows through the flat, placid, meadows beyond the A1. But Cromwell is a strangely isolated backwater. It gives its name to a once powerful family: Ralph de Cromwell was summoned to Parliament in 1375; Ralph, 3rd Lord Cromwell, was High Treasurer of England and built Tattershall Castle (Lincs), Wingfield Castle (Derby) and Lambley Church in this county. There are no relics of the family here: the place passed into the possession of the Holles family of nearby Haughton, Earls of Clare, and so to the Dukes of Newcastle. In overgrown grounds stands the former *Rectory*, a distinguished late 17th-century house, built of brick, but standing on top of the stone undercroft of a Tudor mansion of the Holles; it was the home of three generations of Fynes—Clinton rectors (1789–1911). The *Church* next door has a slender Perp tower, and lofty Dec chancel with great curvilinear E window. Tinted Victorian glass and pitch-pine pews make the interior gloomy, and the chancel is scraped; some fragments of ancient glass, and many High Church ornaments and objects of piety.

Cropwell Bishop [14] On the edge of the Vale of Belvoir, and not far from the Foss. A wide village street, some cottages of local warm-red brick, one older timbered house, and the *Church*. A Perp tower, with double frieze and pinnacles; two low 13th-century arcades in the nave, and a slightly later chancel; old roof (with 17th- and 18th-century dates at random), and old benchends and many pews from the

Colston Bassett old church

Cotham

old church at Colston Bassett: a well-furnished, homely interior. Tablet in chancel to Wm. Marshall, Gent. (1795), signed C. Osborne, Nottm.—'Bonus erat Samaritanus'. The Grantham Canal, much overgrown, makes its inconsequential way through the parish, and two unexpected bottle kilns (as though we were in Staffordshire) stand near by, designed for drying gypsum.

Cuckney [8] The meeting-place of many roads—to Bolsover, to Sheffield, to Worksop, to Ollerton, to Mansfield, as well as a quiet lane into the village itself: there are many Welbeck estate cottages, one or two larger houses, and the *Greendale Oak*. The *Church* has an imposing 13th-century tower, and a long nave of six bays with round arches and a succession of variegated piers, at present all supported by iron splints (1982) for fear of mining subsidence: an impressive, but scraped interior. The churchyard has been stripped of its headstones on the S side and laid out with 'tasteful' flower beds: let us hope that the tombs on the N side survive. A lane to the W leads to Cuckney Lake, with the village school (an old mill) on the bank; along the road towards Ollerton are some of the finest of all Nottinghamshire farm buildings: *Hatfield Grange Farm*. Great brick 18th-century barns with arched entrances form a courtyard, with the farmhouse behind.

Darlton [9] A small ancient settlement in flat forgotten countryside between Tuxford and the Trent: the traffic roars along on the A57, and nobody bothers to stop at little Darlton. There are several good farmhouses, with magnificent brick buildings: *Kingshaugh House* (a short distance to the W) was King John's hunting lodge at this eastern outpost of Sherwood Forest—now but an almost derelict farmhouse awaiting restoration. The *Church*, with its pyramid-topped tower,

appears all Victorian without, but within reveals its medieval arcade and two beautiful little early 16th-century brasses to a knight and his lady, mounted on the sanctuary wall—their identity long forgotten. Victorian glass (by Wailes), and more recent windows, provide a colourful religious atmosphere. Wide views to the Trent, to power stations, and to Lincoln Cathedral.

Drayton, East [9] In a network of minor roads which meander inconsequently through this little-known countryside between Tuxford and the Trent, the *Church* stands at the crossroads, presiding over pleasant groupings of red-brick cottages and farms. A building of some splendour, with many-pinnacled tall tower, long embattled nave and chancel, and elaborate pinnacled porch, its exterior is all Perp, and very handsome. The interior displays earlier origins, with tall 13th-century arcades in the nave—indeed, the church celebrated its 700th anniversary in 1981—a spacious interior, with 15th-century rood screen, 18th-century altar rails, and daylight pouring in through all its clear-glass windows.

Drayton, West [8] The A1 dual carriageway roars past on one side, the little River Maun bubbles along on the other—and beyond that the Old North Road on its way to Retford. West Drayton leads its quiet life in between. There is a cluster of good 18th-century brick houses, a handful of modern bungalows and the little *Church*, its W end protected by ancient yews. A little double bellcote, a Norman S door with holy-water stoup beside it, later Gothic windows elsewhere and, inside, an elegant little organ in a mahogany case. That is all: it is simple but holy, and the churchyard is immaculate. At Markham Moor, close to the roundabout, is the three-storeyed *Markham Moor Inn*, and the *Old Eel Pie House* (now a private house) famous for its eel pies in coaching days.

Dunham-on-Trent [9] The cast-iron toll-bridge carries the A57 into Lincs—built in 1832 by the engineer, George Leather. Grand views up- and downstream and over the little village. The *Church* has a distinguished Perp tower with four enormous windows—like a great lantern; the rest is a remarkably insignificant rebuilding by T.C. Hine of 1862. *Dunham House* was the parochial residence of the prebendary of Dunham in Southwell Minster: it has an attractive 18th-century front, masking an earlier house behind.

Eakring [8] The pretty undulating country between Southwell and Ollerton: the church stands on rising ground, the village street with the *Savile Arms*, and several mellow-brick houses below. J.P. St Aubyn somewhat over-restored the *Church* in 1880; an old photograph shows its former state. The EE and Perp tower, aisleless nave, and chancel contain a few medieval fragments, a 17th-century pulpit, a 17th-century font, and two stone Royal Arms of Elizabeth I (from a house in the village) inserted in the N porch. There is a crumbling 17th-century monument (the Dand family), and a Victorian brass plate and stained glass in the chancel to the memory of William Mompesson, the 'plague' Rector of Eyam (Derbyshire) who so faithfully ministered to his flock there in 1665-6. He was subsequently translated by Sir George Savile of Rufford to this parish (1670), but his new flock at first boycotted his services: he was obliged to live in a shack in Rufford Park, and conduct services under an ash tree, called the *Pulpit Ash*, in a field, where the 1st Lord Savile later erected a cross to mark the site. Mompesson lived down his 'plague' reputation, was incumbent here for 38 years, and a Prebendary of Southwell. He declined the Deanery of Lincoln. S of the village, on the pretty lane that leads to Kirklington, are the headquarters of the BP Notting-

hamshire oilfield—a few low-lying buildings and sheds. Oil was first discovered here in 1933 and elsewhere in Notts in the years following. For many years the 'nodding donkeys' were to be seen in the fields round here, quietly chugging away, pumping the oil from deep wells: none here now, but there are some to be seen elsewhere in the N of the county.

East Bridgford, *see* Bridgford, East

East Drayton, *see* Drayton, East

East Leake, *see* Leake, East

East Markham, *see* Markham, East

East Stoke, *see* Stoke, East

Eastwood [10] 'I was born in Eastwood,' wrote D.H. Lawrence, 'a mining village of some three thousand souls, about eight miles from Nottingham, and one mile from the small stream, the Erewash, which divides Nottinghamshire from Derbyshire. It is hilly country, looking west to Crich and towards Matlock, sixteen miles away, and east and north-east towards Mansfield and the Sherwood Forest district. To me it seemed, and still seems, an extremely beautiful countryside, just between the red sandstone and the oak trees of Nottingham, and the cold limestone, the ash trees, the stone fences of Derbyshire.' Lawrence was born at *8a Victoria Street* in 1885. The road from Nottingham leads up into the somewhat drab main street: past the Library, Victoria Street is the fifth on the right. No 8a has been restored and furnished and filled with Lawrence souvenirs, and is

◁ *above* **Dunham-on-Trent**
below at **Costock**

top **Cuckney**
centre at **Eastwood** Hall ▷
bottom at Harfield Grange
near **Cuckney**

Erewash canal at Eastwood

inspired and coloured all his writing. Another holy place, but this time for train lovers, is the *Sun Inn*, at the crossroads beyond Victoria Street—known as the birthplace of the Midland Railway. In 1832 a meeting was held here of local colliery owners to discuss the carrying of their coal: first the Midland Counties Railway was formed; then the Midland Railway itself came into being, connecting not only the local towns and collieries, but Birmingham, Bristol and London. *Eastwood Hall* stands along the road to Underwood—an early 19th-century stuccoed house, once the home of the coal-owning Walker family, now local offices of the NCB. Behind are some very handsome quadrangular farm buildings. There was a medieval church, then an 18th-century building; only the tower of the Victorian *Church* which replaced this (in 1858) survives: the rest was burnt down by vandals in 1963. A new church has been built. The Plumptre family have been patrons since 1689: there were four Plumptre rectors between 1829 and 1907. Past the church there are several old houses, and as the street descends to the Erewash there are one or two old farms and cottages. There are delightful walks across the river and along the canal: all vintage Lawrence country.

Eaton [5] The Old North Road (to Retford) skirts the village: a quiet lane of red-brick cottages leads to the little Victorian *Church* (by George Shaw, 1858) in the Dec style, with a painted bellcote. *Eaton Hall* is a white-painted stuccoed, early 19th-century house, with pretty cast-iron balconies, built by the Simpsons of Babworth: many new buildings in the grounds (1950s onwards, for the Teacher Training College). Beyond the church the lane leads down to the River Idle, and crosses the bridge to the quiet countryside beyond. 'Eaton' is a corruption of 'Idleton'.

open to the public. His father was a miner, working at Brinsley colliery; his mother kept a small shop in the front room, selling linen and baby clothes to eke out their slender resources. The family moved in 1887 to *28 Garden Road* (at the bottom of Victoria Street, a short walk down Princes Street—and across Wood Street a footpath leads into Garden Road); here No 28 has been opened as a Museum, administered by the Association of Young Writers. In 1891 the Lawrences moved to *Walker Street* (the other side of the school grounds from Garden Road): 'Go to Walker Street,' wrote Lawrence, 'and stand in front of the third house—and look across at Crich on the left, Underwood in front—High Park Woods and Annesley on the right.

I lived in that house from the age of 6 to 18, and I know that view better than any in the world . . . that is the country of my heart.' The local countryside, the local scenes, moulded Lawrence: it was about these that he wrote. Many of the landmarks in his novels may be recognized here; he went from the local school with a scholarship to Nottingham High School, and then to University College, Nottingham. It was at Haggs Farm, home of his friend Jessie Chambers, a little N of the Moorgreen Reservoir, where he first conceived the idea of writing: 'a tiny farm on the edge of the Wood. That was Miriam's farm, where I got my first incentive to write.' Lawrence left Eastwood in 1908, and died at Vence in France in 1930. But it was Eastwood that

Eaton

Edingley [11] Gently undulating country: the 'back' road to Mansfield from Southwell. A small village of red-brick cottages, and a diminutive *Church*, which has lost its NW tower and S aisle: Norman W door, and one tiny Norman window, other features 14th century; charmingly furnished interior, with little 19th-century painting (apparently by a boy of 10) showing the old tower. A great sycamore by the church gate, and many old tombstones.

Edwalton [14] A few old houses in the street—but the village is now more or less part of West Bridgford, with prosperous houses of the pre- or post-war era lining the leafy roads; *Edwalton Hall* (now an hotel) was built by the architect

A.W. Brewill for himself; it is an imposing Edwardian house. The *Church* stands on the edge of open country: its special attraction is the 16th-century brick tower, reminiscent of a church in Essex. Small medieval nave, with 14th-century S arcade and earlier N wall. A rood screen leads into the chancel rebuilt by Brewill (in brick) on the old foundations; its predecessor collapsed in the 17th century. A well-furnished, much loved, little building.

Edwinstowe [8] Coal, and the charms of Sherwood Forest, vie with one another here. From early times the clearing in the forest, and the village that grew up round the chantry built close to the burial place of King Edwin (killed in bat-

tle, 633) made Edwinstowe the most important forest settlement. The coal-mines have now closed in on the place, and the great mine (first sunk in 1925) dominates it. But charm remains in the old village; there is an ancient and notable *Church*; and the street leads N into the heart of the Forest, to the *Major Oak* itself. The great solid 12th-century tower, crowned with its broach spire and cluster of unusual pinnacles (probably a rebuilding of 1680) is awe inspiring; the clerestoried nave, the aisles, the chancel, all embattled, give the impression of a Perp church, but inside there are earlier arcades and a quantity of dark Victorian glass. There is an odd little Victorian mausoleum to the Ward family, attached to the N aisle, a Foljambe

Egmanton

Elston Towers

memorial window in the chancel by Heaton, Butler and Bayne (see Ollerton), and a tablet in the S aisle to William Villa Real (d.1759), member of a family of Portuguese Jews who settled here in the 18th century. The Revd F.C. Day Lewis, father of the late Poet Laureate, was Vicar of Edwinstowe, 1918–38. N of the church, *Edwinstowe Hall*, a large square 18th-century house, is now a County Council Children's Home. The road leads on into the Forest: a group of hexagonal huts forms an attractive 'centre' for visitors—and here, and at the Major Oak (its trunk is 32 ft round), the memory of Robin Hood may be venerated. The coming of the railway in the 19th century first brought an influx of visitors to the forest; for them the Dukeries Hotel—close to the railway—with its display of timbering and bow windows, was built in the 1890s. The opening of the colliery brought an enormous increase in population, new housing estates, and a cinema. But the poor old 30s' cinema is now the 'Major Divan Centre'.

Egmanton [8] A holy place: here, in little-visited countryside, is Nottinghamshire's Shrine of Our Lady.

The village is small and unassuming, approached by quiet lanes: cottages, a farmhouse or two, gardens and orchards, Egmanton Wood to the S, and, behind the farm next to the church, a steep mound—all that remains of a motte and bailey castle. The *Church* is small and unassuming, too—outside—with a Nottinghamshire tower, S transept, and no porch. But inside, this is no ordinary church. The interior is ablaze with colour, aglow with candles and lighted tapers—a medieval church redecked and redecorated by Sir Ninian Comper. Over the doorway, in a gallery high against the S wall, is the organ, gloriously decorated and gilded; across the chancel arch a magnifical rood screen, with gallery, painted panels, the Rood and attendant figures; there are altars in the chapels, a painted pulpit, other objects of piety. In 1896 the 7th Duke of Newcastle, reviving an ancient cult, re-established the Shrine of Our Lady of Egmanton, and in a happy partnership with Comper restored and redecorated the church. Through the screen, a gorgeous Comper High Altar, a Comper E window, and on the N side of the chancel, the Shrine itself, the figure of the Virgin under a canopy, candles, lamps, and flowers. As for the church itself, the N arcade is 12th century, there are fragments of ancient glass in the transept, old pews, an early effigy and a small colourful Jacobean monument and a 16th-century incised slab in the sanctuary. Pilgrimages are held here in the summer, and the whole place is soaked in the prayers of the faithful. Egmanton is a church to pray in.

Elkesley [8] The *Church* tower peers over the houses of the village, over the fences and hedges which protect it from the roaring traffic of the A1 by-pass; the small village is a little world apart. A wide Perp arch in the base of the tower serves as a porch: the interior is pleasing with its early 19th-century W gallery and fittings; there is no chancel arch, and at the junction of nave and chancel are two decorative niches—the upper one an entrance to a long-vanished rood loft. The building is chiefly early 14th century: old roof; modest 18th- and 19th-century tablets to the Sharpe family.

Elston [11] The building called *Elston Towers*, standing at the corner of the Foss Way, makes an extraordinary introduction to the place. It looks like some minor waterworks: in fact it was built as a private house, in 1875. It is something of a Victorian joke, with its large Gothic traceried windows, tower-like projections at either end and a roof sprouting with metal ornaments; behind there was at one time a clock tower and a Baptist chapel, but the clock tower was replaced by a tall metal chimney when the house was for a time used as a maggot factory: the story is as fantastic as the house itself. The village lies away from the main road, secluded in its own lanes, with unsophisticated cottages, and a rash of smart neo-Georgian villas. The *Church* with its tall, narrow tower and pinnacled exterior looks like a dolls' house church; it is a medieval building, much done over in the 19th century. But the great thing is the array of Darwin monuments; the gifted and learned family of Darwin came here (by marriage) in the 17th century: Dr Erasmus Darwin was born here in 1731; Charles Darwin, author of *The Origin of Species*, was his grandson. There are several very decorative monuments of the 17th and 18th centuries, and a particularly fine display of early 19th-century white marble tablets in the N aisle (three by Tiley of Bristol, one by Taylor of York). High up over the tower arch is a memorial to George Lascelles (d.1616), and the arch itself is decorated with many shields of his and allied families (the Lascelles were connections of the Darwins). *Elston Hall*, home of the Darwins till 1951, has a long, late 17th-century stone front, with central porch and gabled wings, an entertaining carved figure rising from the cresting of the porch; an 18th-century pedimented front door and sash windows give the house a Georgian look. Long wings at either end, added when the house became a prep school, make the house even longer; it is now divided into flats. In a field, approached by a back lane to the NE, stands the

ancient Elston chapel, at one time a separate parish. Unused for many decades, derelict and vandalized in recent years, the little building has now been taken over by the Redundant Churches Fund, and partially restored. There is a Norman doorway, and much Norman and later medieval masonry; little, alas, remains of the charming Georgian fittings, so wantonly left to decay in recent years.

Elton [15] At the crossroads on the Grantham–Nottingham road (A52): an 18th-century gateway to a vanished house, the church, a few cottages, the *Manor Arms*, an early 19th-century Old Rectory (with a heraldic, Gothic dining-room inside), a farm with a splendid barn—and an arcaded wall stretching to the main road. A charming little *Church* with stuccoed exterior: the S aisle was demolished in the late 18th century (and the Norman arcade blocked up); old clear glass, 17th-century altar rails, monuments to the Launder and Norton families, and hatchments; the tomb to Mrs Launder outside the chancel is inscribed with a delightful epitaph in Latin elegiacs. The Manor was demolished in 1933: it was a large, plain, 18th-century stuccoed house, with sash windows and castellated parapets, built (or enlarged) by Cornelius Launder in the 1780s; it descended by marriage to the Nortons. The great brick walls of the kitchen garden survive, and the topiary garden and orchards surrounding Manor Cottage are beautifully maintained: along the lane to Granby the little toy-fort *gazebo* peers over the wall, and there is a *cottage* opposite with a mouth-watering Gothick porch. There is a station—Elton and Orston—on the line from Grantham to Nottingham: it is a pleasure sometimes to take to the train, and enjoy the Vale of Belvoir from the carriage window.

Epperstone [11] The pretty road from Gonalston, and a pretty *village*

street: many old cottages, and some larger houses—like the Old Rectory, and the Manor, which with its attractive Victorian–Tudor features, seems to line the whole length of one side of the street. Opposite the *Cross Keys* is a tall, rectangular, gabled brick dovecote. The *Church* stands opposite the Manor, with its plain 14th-century spire—and nave and chancel barbarously re-covered recently in red concrete tiles. Inside, a 13th-century arcade; monuments to the Huskinson family (who built the Manor), and rather dark Victorian glass; the church was much restored in 1853. The village is protected on the S side by the by-pass, which carries the heavy traffic from Gunthorpe Bridge.

Everton [5] The traffic roars by on the busy A631 (Gainsborough to Bawtry), but the back lanes of the village are quiet, and contain a number of old brick houses and cottages. Here stands the *Church*: the lower stages of the tower are Norman, and there is a crudely carved early Norman tympanum over the S door; tower arch and chancel arch are Norman too, and the small apsidal E end of the chancel (built in 1841) gives the impression of a Norman apsidal church. The nave clerestory and the upper part of the tower are Perp. Wide views everywhere—over gentle undulating Notts to the S, and across flat empty carrs towards Yorkshire in the N.

Farndon [12] There is a smudge of bungalows bordering the Foss, almost linking the village to Newark—but the *old village* is a delight, with its many Georgian houses, its high brick walls. The Old Hall is three-storeyed and dignified; Farndon Lodge, next to the church, is two-storeyed and square, with a stone Doric portico, and a brick gazebo overlooking the lawn. The outside of the *Church* is plastered all over, but on the N wall a patch has been removed to reveal

Three views at **Fiskerton**

the Saxon or early Norman herringbone masonry; the tower was rebuilt in 1598 – 'this was done Ao 1598' records an inscription, and adds the names of the churchwardens and builders. Inside, the S arcade is EE, the N was rebuilt by Hodgson Fowler, who restored the church in 1890; the chancel is dim and religious behind a lofty Victorian screen; there is good Victorian glass and woodwork. A Saxon sword, inside the stone coffin which was discovered at the time of the restoration (now in the N aisle), is now preserved in the British Museum. To the W a lane leads down to the Trent: a ferry used to ply between here and Rolleston.

Farnsfield [11] A large village, on the 'back' road to Mansfield from Southwell: a village street with many good cottages and larger houses, and an astonishing 19th-century *Church*, which towers over all. Built in 1869 by T.C. Hine, with lofty nave, tall dormered clerestory windows, apsidal chancel, dominating, prickly, slate-covered squat spire at the SW corner, it is a magnificent monstrosity, looking more like a church in a Victorian suburb than a village church; it is Hine at his most exuberant. The base of the tower is in fact early 15th century. The interior is imposing and spacious, with three windows of the apse by Wailes. To the N of the village is *Hexgreave Park*, one of the Archbishop of York's medieval hunting parks: there is a good-looking 18th-century brick house (now a private residence) deep in its beech woods, with commanding views towards Southwell.

Finningley [2] 'We were pushed over into Yorkshire in the reorganization' said a woman in the church, 'and against our will; we still consider ourselves Nottinghamshire, and we are in the diocese of Southwell.' So much for Whitehall. It is frontier country, part of the parish having always been in the West Riding, and it remains disputed territory today. The *Church* is a prize worth fighting for, with its Norman tower, Norman doorway, Dec chancel, and original timber roof in nave and chancel: it also has a pulpit dated 1603, a 17th-century font cover, and excellent oak pews, perhaps by Hodgson Fowler who restored the church at the end of the last century. There is a curious late 17th-century painted memorial in the vestry; the marble monument to the Revd Edmund Harvey, STP (1828), with its garlands, might be taken for work of the mid 18th century. The Harveys held the manor from the 18th century until the 20th: John Harvey of Ickwell Bury, Beds, endowed the school—an attractive converted barn, now used as the village hall. The enormous RAF station is in Yorkshire. These are flat lands, drained in the 17th century by Cornelius Vermuyden, who owned land here; the road E leads to Wroot, that desolate spot in the Isle of Axholme, Lincs.

Fiskerton-cum-Morton [11] There is something of the character of a village on the Thames here, with one or two large early 19th-century houses standing in shady gardens behind high brick walls. A path leads down to the Trent, where boats are tied up—with, maybe, a barge or two beached outside a chandler's shop—and the *Bromley Arms* looks across the broad sweep of the river to East Stoke opposite. Downstream, the road to Rolleston hugs the river bank, and commands spectacular views. Near by, Fiskerton Mill, a tall four-storeyed brick building, stands astride the Halloughton Dumble close to where it joins the Trent. A short distance inland, Morton is a gathering of lanes and cottages clustering round a small red-brick *Church* of 1756, with round-headed windows, a shallow apsidal sanctuary and an embattled tower; unfortunately it has lost its original fittings, and the windows have been 'Lombardized' and filled with tinted glass. And further inland still, *Fiskerton Station* is a delightful little cottage *ornée*, built in 1849 for the Midland Railway (Newark–Nottingham line).

Flawborough [12] From its low hill there is a wide view: the lane descends slowly and, before it turns, a great prospect of the Vale may be surveyed, the countryside opening up like an enormous saucer. The *Church* stands on its little summit: warm red brick of 1841, with pinnacled tower and Gothick windows, a Norman W doorway from the former church, and a quiet, plastered interior; a well-kept churchyard, too, with many slate headstones. There are two or three good farmhouses in the village—one with a weather-vane on its roof; Newcastle Cottage is part stone, part warm red brick, part stucco, and sprucely thatched.

Fledborough [9] The vast low-lying dank meadows accompanying the Trent become ever more lonely and deserted: along the W bank stand the monster power stations, and crouching below are small remote villages with low church towers and red-brick cottages, rarely visited by travellers from the outside world. Such a place is Fledborough. 'In the early part of the last century' writes Francis White in his *Nottinghamshire Directory* (1853) 'this place obtained the apellation of the Gretna Green of Nottinghamshire, from the Rector (a Mr Sweetapple), who like the blacksmith of the Scottish border fettered with the chain of wedlock all who applied to him for that happy purpose.' Indeed any irregularity might be imagined here. A very special *church*—of somewhat forlorn beauty: spacious Dec nave, with wide aisles, an earlier tower, and a chancel, long ruinous, rebuilt by Pearson in 1891; two surviving carved panels of an Easter sepulchre; several 13th- and 14th-century tombs, speaking of the earlier importance of the place; and a considerable quantity of 14th-century glass. Many windows contain whole sections: of special note is the E window of the N aisle, where the centre light is filled with stone, bearing a carved canopied niche for a statue. Only a narrow, dead-end lane connects Fledborough with the outside world; there are only two or three houses: beyond the church flows the great river.

Flintham [11] The casual, unsuspecting visitor may be astonished, when driving through the village, to espy at the end of the street what appears to be part of the Crystal Palace, marvellously removed to Nottinghamshire. Inspired by the Crystal Palace it may be, but it is in fact the great *Conservatory* of Flintham Hall. Driving N along the Foss, there is a glimpse through the trees of a great Victorian house with, apparently, a wing of the Crystal Palace affixed to its E end. *Flintham* is indeed one of the most evocative of all 19th-century houses, still lived in, loved and cherished as a private house; but it is in origin a much older house. An old picture shows a gabled house of the 17th-century, incorporating the great hall of a medieval building; part of the brickwork of this survives in the wing behind the conservatory. This old house, home of Husseys, Hackers and Disneys, was purchased in 1789 by Colonel Thomas Thoroton of Screveton (q.v.), great great great nephew of Dr Robert Thoroton, the historian of Nottinghamshire. He rebuilt the house in 1798 and it was enlarged by Lewis Wyatt in 1820. His son married the heiress of Sir Robert D'Arcy Hildyard, last baronet of Winestead in the E Riding. It was for his son Thomas Blackborne Thoroton Hildyard, MP, that T.C. Hine remodelled the house between 1853 and 1859. The late Georgian brick wings and stable yard survive at the back; Hine encased the front in stone, in his own inimitable style, built the tower at the W end, and

the library and conservatory at the other. T.B.T. Hildyard's sister had married Sir John Thorold, 11th Bt of Syston, across the border in Lincolnshire: they had a great library and a great conservatory (built in the previous generation), so the Hildyards had to have both, and the conservatory at Flintham is indeed the most spectacular in England. Flintham reborn put the Thorolds in their place; but in fact both families were almost ruined by their houses. Syston was pulled down; the builder of Flintham was forced to live abroad. Flintham in its glorious Victorian dress, even until recently, was not much admired by the neighbours. Now, incredibly, Flintham has come into its own: thanks to the present squire, Mr Myles Thoroton Hildyard, himself an antiquary and president of the Thoroton Society, and to Mr David Rowbotham, the house, gloriously revived, has more friends and admirers than ever before. Hine's fantastic entrance tower welcomes the arriving guest, the rooms are filled with Holland's furniture made for them, the *Library* overflows with books—and from its gallery there is access to the romantic balcony which overlooks the conservatory, with its fountain and exotic plants. The *Church* nestles under the shadow of the conservatory: the central tower is 12th and 13th century; the rest was mostly rebuilt in 1828. There are fragments of old heraldic glass, and magnificent Thoroton hatchments. The village is attractive with its long street of cottages and larger houses, built of warm red Nottinghamshire brick.

Gamston [8] The road to Retford: gentle undulating countryside. Red-brick cottages and larger houses—the Pelham buckle on a porch here or there denotes a former Newcastle village. The grand Perp tower of the *Church* presides over all. Outside, it appears all Perp with low embattled chancel, high embattled nave, and circular NE

turret to rood loft and roof. Inside, S arcade and low chancel arch are earlier: the high blank space above it calls for a gorgeous rood screen and crucifix by Comper. Two or three early effigies and later marble tablets to former rectors. At the N end of the village a large Georgian (and later) house, with many outbuildings, with goal posts (or cricket pitches in summer) in the meadows below, could only be a prep school; it is Bramcote school.

Gedling [11] The *great spire* of Gedling is one of the sights of Notts, built in the early 14th century and rising to a tremendous height above humdrum streets and suburban housing—for Gedling is now submerged in the outskirts of Nottingham. The tower is embattled, and the spire rises from its broaches with a remarkable entasis: this, and its clean lines—there are no pinnacles and no crockets—give it its powerful appeal. A notable *Church*, too: the tower stands at the NW corner of the nave so the Dec nave is lit by a W window; the clerestory is Perp, the long chancel EE, with lancet windows. Splendid 18th-century candelabra, and five hatchments (recently restored) of the Stanhopes, Earls of Chesterfield (of nearby Shelford); EE sedilia, aumbry, piscina in the chancel. Two famous Notts cricketers are buried in the churchyard: Arthur Shrewsbury, whom Dr Grace called the greatest batsman of his age, and Alfred Shaw 'the emperor of bowlers'. Gedling House is an elegant late 18th-century stuccoed house overlooking the Trent Valley, now a school; to the NW is the great colliery (opened in 1904); the road past the church climbs the hill steeply, past the colliery, up to *Mapperley Plains*. There are dramatic views from the top with Gedling spire in the distance far below.

Girton [9] For a short distance the Notts–Lincs frontier, which zigzags now E, now W, to put North Scarle

Flawborough

in Lincs, South Scarle in Notts, runs along the main road from Newark to Gainsborough (A1133): Girton is just in Notts. A diminutive village with a diminutive church, its back lane leads nowhere but the flat meadows bordering the little River Fleet and, beyond that, the Trent. The Fleet, following the old course of the Trent, is for the most part a stream, but at Girton it widens out to become almost a lake. The little church with bellcote is ancient, but was much restored by Ewan Christian in 1879.

Gonalston [11] A delightful backwater by-passed by the Nottingham–Southwell road (A612): old brick houses—such as *Manor Farm* and the *Old Kennels*—and old cottages, too. The estate has only changed hands once by sale since the Conquest (in 1537), and has been cherished by generations of the Francklin family. The *Church* is approached down a grass path, accompanied by a tiny stream, past the garden of the Old Rectory: Victorian outside, with NW tower by T.C. Hine (1853), it is unexpectedly ancient within, with three early 14th-century effigies of the de Heriz family, discovered by the sculptor Richard Westmacott in 1848, buried in a pit under the nave, where they had been thrown on the demolition of the N aisle in 1797. Hine rebuilt the aisle, and the effigies were reinstalled. Fragments of ancient glass; 17th-century altar rails; 18th-century pulpit; and a gorgeous deep blue 19th-century window in the nave. A medieval altar slab came from the chapel of the Spital of St Mary Magdalene (which stood to the E of the village). W of the church are the grassy mounds of the ancient Manor: the Monux family, who purchased from the de Heriz in 1537, made their principal home in Bedfordshire, with only a hunting lodge and stables here. In 1807 Richard Francklin married the heiress of Sir Philip Monux, last Bt, and in 1851 T.C. Hine enlarged the old Hunting

In the conservatory, **Flintham**

Lodge, which adjoined the stables, in a fine position above the church: built of stone, with characteristic Hine–Gothic windows and copper-covered flèche, the new building adjoins the old brick house and commands a wide view of the Trent Valley and the Vale of Belvoir. At the S end of the village a late 18th-century brick water-mill stands astride the Dover Beck; after being derelict for some years, it has recently been converted into a house.

Gotham [13] (pronounced Goat'm) A large, spreading village, in the wolds S of Nottingham, and in the smoke of the local gypsum works (successors to the celebrated alabaster mines), with the brooding presence of Ratcliffe power station near by: its mammoth chimney and gargantuan cooling towers peer over the hills to the W. Gotham has legendary fame on account of the dotty stories of its Wise Men of early days. Prominent *Church*, with very early broach spire (13th century), Perp clerestory, stuccoed aisles, chancel of 1789, and odd hipped roof to the nave. Inside, interesting 13th-century S arcade; in the chancel early 17th-century alabaster monuments to the St Andrew family, facing each other; later monuments to incumbents—one to the Revd John Bridges 'Rector of this church, Presented thereto by ye renowned Loyalist William first Duke of Newcastle, His Grace. Anno 1678'. At E end of the church stands an early 17th-century brick gabled manor house, with barge boards and later windows, set amid farm buildings and high walls. *The Cuckoo Bush Inn* recalls the Wise Men, who attempted to entrap a cuckoo within high hedges; to their surprise the bird promptly flew away, leaving them to other follies.

Granby [14] The name, and often the portrait, of the Marquis of Granby is displayed on many an inn-sign, all over England. But who knows where Granby is, here in Nottinghamshire, in the Vale of Belvoir? Not a soul. Church and village stand delightfully on a low escarpment surveying the Vale, surveying the Castle. When the 9th Earl of Rutland was, in 1703, created Duke of Rutland, he was also created Marquis of Granby—the title always held by the eldest son. It was John, eldest son of the 3rd Duke, who was C-in-C of the British forces in Germany, and a popular hero among all ranks, who became patron saint of so many public houses. He died in 1770, in his father's lifetime: his son became 4th Duke. Granby, now a mere village, was once of more importance as a small market town: the demolished N aisle of the church, the blocked-up arcade, are evidence of its decline. What remains of the *Church* is spacious, but scraped. The base of the tower is Norman, the upper part Perp; otherwise, much 14th-century work, and some 17th- and 18th-century furnishings; of some interest are the remains of the terracotta tracery of the E window (a great rarity)—now lying in the chancel—the terracotta replaced by stone in a Victorian restoration. Some pretty cottages: the public house is, of course, the *Marquis of Granby*.

Greasley [10] Surprisingly rural, despite the proximity of Nottingham, and all else. *Castle Farm* is a good 18th-century farmhouse and incorporated in the farm buildings are fragments of the walls and bastions of the castle of the Cantilupes. The *Church* has a grand many-pinnacled Perp tower; the rest is an imposing and original rebuilding—'Earl Cowper, the Duke of Rutland and Barber, Walker & Co defrayed the cost of the restoration of this church in 1896' reads a tablet near the tower—Barber, Walker & Co were the great local coal-owners. There are slate commandment boards, and beautiful fragments of medieval glass from Beauvale Priory (q.v.)—roundels of St Agatha and St Lucy—in the chancel. A 17th-century monument in the S aisle commemorates Lancelot Rolleston: 'In memory of Lancelot Rolleston of Watnall in the Co. of Nottm. Esqre. for his knowne and steddy loyalty to his Prince he was made High Sheriff of this county in the year 1682. A gentleman generally belov'd in his country, but especially by his particular acquaintance. He was a great lover of the particular person yt once he contracted friendship with, and not given to change'; he died in 1685, aged 34. Near by the E window of the aisle 'taken from Watnall Hall is placed here by members of his family in loving and honoured memory of Lancelot Rolleston, K.C.B., D.S.O., a Magistrate for 70 years, born 1848, died 1941, the last of his line to live at Watnall Hall'. There are coats of arms, and a small picture of the house—a late 17th-century building, with very fine iron gates, and handsome period interiors. All was lost, and a housing estate now occupies the site; a broken fragment of the gates stands at the head of the drive, on the main road into Nottingham.

Gringley-on-the-Hill [5] Some hill—for flat, far-flung, northernmost Notts: the quiet lowlands watered by the Idle lie below to the S, and the immense emptiness of the carrs adjoining Yorkshire to the N. Gringley is an appealing village with many lanes, many red-brick cottages, many farms with immense buildings, barns, dovecotes. The *Church* is appealing too; there is a Norman door in the base of the tower, the upper part Perp of familiar Notts type, and there is an unexpected 17th-century door in the N aisle. Inside, a tall EE N arcade, a spacious N aisle, an exceptional EE shaft piscina, and a tactfully rebuilt early 20th-century S aisle; there are good modern furnishings, too—screen, stalls, W gallery. On the walk back down churchyard path to village street there is a great *panorama* of rich farmlands below, stretching on and on as far as the eye can see.

Grove [5] The spire of Grove church is clearly visible on the low undulating hills SE of Retford; a narrow lane leads up to the village. The great house was pulled down in 1951: a broad drive leads to its magnificent site on the *escarpment*, with wide views over the countryside to S and W. The great families of Hersey, Neville, Levinz, Eyre and Harcourt-Vernon lived here; John Smythson, Carr of York, and Repton worked here; now the site is occupied by low broiler buildings, and the old stable buildings, somewhat down at heel, stand behind. The kennels of the Grove Hunt have been moved to Serlby, Grove has become a forgotten village, and few visit it. In May 1982 the current page in the Church visitors' book began with signatures of visitors in 1978—among them a Harcourt-Vernon. Old sporting pictures exist of the Grove Hunt, with horses and hounds in the park, and John Carr's mansion behind— a white stuccoed house, with bay window in the centre of the long S front. This was built in 1762; behind stood part of the earlier house, and John Smythson's plan exists (entitled 'Mr Neville's house of Grove'), showing an Elizabethan house with porch and Great Hall. Repton made improvements in 1790. The *Church* was rebuilt in 1882, a typical scholarly work of Hodgson Fowler: it contains an incised slab to Hugh Hersey and his wife (a Leeke) of 1455. The Eyre monuments are at Rampton. To the N of the village the road to North Leverton carries on along the top of the hill, commanding a great view of the three enormous power stations along the River Trent.

Gunthorpe [11] The new bridge over the Trent was opened by Edward Prince of Wales in 1927. The river is alive with boats; there is a public house, a restaurant or two, a small church of 1849, and *Gunthorpe Hall*, a captivating 18th-century white-painted tall stuccoed house with battlements and crenel-

lations and lower residential wing, looking like a minor Scottish castle on the Dee.

Halam [11] Charmingly set under the plantations of Norwood Park: the village street leads off the Southwell–Mansfield road. Many attractive red-brick cottages, and a few larger houses: *Manor Farm* is an 18th-century stone house, occupying the site of the ancient manor house of the Leekes; there are handsome farm buildings, barn and dovecote. The little *Church* has an early squat tower with low pyramid roof; inside, Norman chancel arch, and 14th-century glass in the chancel, Morris glass in the nave. A few pretty monuments in the chancel: one in the Gothick taste is to Thomas Wright (1848), builder of Upton Hall (q.v.).

Halloughton [11] Just off the main road from Southwell to Nottingham (A612)—a delectable spot: a dead-end lane 'Halloughton only', a few cottages, a farmhouse or two, and the lane peters out in the fields, in the wide open countryside between here and Westhorpe. The little church has a 13th-century E end with small lancets; the rest is a very good imitation by Ewan Christian (1879), using a number of old features. Small W bellcote, 15th-century screen. Opposite stands a very special house, even by Nottinghamshire standards: a very pleasant stuccoed seven-bay *Georgian farmhouse* and, attached to it on the E side, a tremendous medieval stone tower house, dating back to the 13th century. It is a perfect marriage. It was a prebendal house of Southwell, and the whole delightful composition looks S across a wide lawn to the gentle tumbling country of the Trent Valley.

Harby [9] A desolate spot in the middle of nowhere—Nottinghamshire's easternmost outpost, with the Lincolnshire frontier only a few fields away, and views of

the domes of Doddington Hall across the wooded landscape to the E. On 27th November 1290 there died here Queen Eleanor, wife of Edward I: her memorial or 'Eleanor' crosses were erected at the places where her body lay on the way to burial in Westminster Abbey (Geddington, Hardingstone, Waltham Cross, Charing Cross). She fell ill here, at the manor house of Richard de Weston, in September and died in November. The chantry chapel which the king built here disappeared long ago: the moated site of the manor house can only be dimly discerned. But the Victorians made good these losses by building a grand *Church* here in 1875 (J.T. Lee of London, architect), the gift of the Jarvis family of Doddington Hall. The Norman door to the vestry, and a medieval font survive from the old church; the present building is vintage Victorian: a reredos brilliant with mosaics (by Powell & Co), a tiled sanctuary, an imposing organ designed for its position (a magnificent piece of furniture), stained glass by Heaton and Butler, pulpit—even a Victorian velvet altar frontal. An inscription on the sanctuary step reads 'Here died Eleanor of Castile, Queen of England, November 27 1290'. Her statue gazes out from a niche over the tower doorway: above her rises a tall shingled spire, a prominent landmark across the flat, lonely, landscape.

Harworth [5] The Yorkshire border to the N, the Doncaster by-pass (A1M) to the W, the great slag heap of the colliery to the S: within this small triangle is the old village. The *Church* stands on a little hillock, with grand views to the slag heap, and to the splendid tower of Tickhill Church across the border. There was much rebuilding by C.J. Neale in 1869 when the transepts were added; the Norman features are all much restored, but the pinnacled Perp tower survives (typically Notts). To the W the

Halloughton

new colliery village spreads out—
a sprawl of suburban roads.

Haughton [8] A *ruined chapel* by a
lonely stream: that is all that is left
of the great house of the Holles
family, which has passed almost
into oblivion, but for an engraving
by Kip, showing a great Tudor
palace with the little chapel near
by. Sir William Holles, Lord Mayor
of London (1539) and Master of the
Mercers' Company, was the
founder of the family; his son 'the
good Sir William' (so known for his
acts of kindness and hospitality)
bought the old Stanhope property
of Haughton and built or rebuilt
the great house in 1545, adorned
with his device of a holly branch
with clusters of berries. His grandson was created Earl of Clare in
1624, and the 2nd Earl married
Lady Margaret Cavendish,
daughter and heiress of the 2nd
Duke of Newcastle (first creation),
and the dukedom was revived for
him. The rest of the complicated

Halam

78

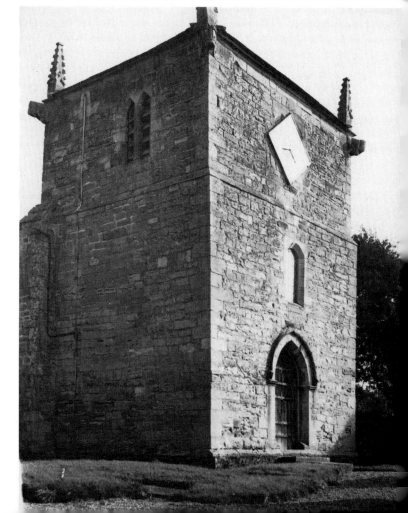

Haughton: Park House

story of the Pelham-Holles, Pelham-Clinton family is told under Clumber (q.v.): as Clumber rose, Haughton fell, and was finally demolished in the 18th century. Haughton Hall Farm, with its great farm buildings, occupies the site; a few ancient trees of the park survive, and a railway line carries goods traffic to the colliery at Bevercotes; the ruins of the little Norman chapel moulder by the River Maun. But a short distance to the N, on a fine site, stands *Haughton Park House*, a square double-pile brick house of *c*.1700, with sash windows and white-painted cupola—quite one of the most delightsome houses in Notts. Nearer the A1 *Haughton Old School*, a brick building of 1692, now a private house, stands close to the road to Gamston, turning its back

on the main road: another charmer.

Hawksworth [11] A village of unexpected pleasures. The *Church* has an early 18th-century brick tower, but built into the S side is an awe-inspiring Norman tympanum: 'Gauterus et uxor eius Cecilina fecerunt facere ecclesiam istam . . .' (why istam?) reads the inscription; the nave and wide N aisle were rebuilt in the 18th century, the chancel in 1851—the chancel dark with Victorian glass (by Wailes). At the E end of the church stands a large white Regency house; on the S side, an iron gate with brick gatepiers leads to a stable quadrangle with tall dovecote tower. On the W side are the capacious brick farm buildings of Hall Farm, dated 1820 in blue brick. There are many

attractive cottages and at the end of the street is the *Manor House*, a low 16th-century stone building, with gabled porch and Gothick glazing bars. The post office sells excellent Stilton cheese and many other unexpected delicacies. Belvoir countryside, of wide views and unsophisticated charms.

Hawton [12] The flat meadows of the River Devon—gypsum workings near by: the great pinnacled tower of the *Church* rises in its splendour above the houses of the little village, the church itself distinguished, the chancel among the great showpieces of any village church anywhere. The tower was built at the end of the 15th century by Sir Thomas Molyneux, whose arms appear in the spandrels of the W doorway: the door itself is

79

Hayton

original, with fragments of its carved inscription 'Jesu Mercy, Mary Help'; the clerestory of the nave is also of this date. Inside, the arcades are 13th century and there is a 15th-century screen—but the eye is dazzled by the great Dec E window with its curvilinear tracery, and the glories of the chancel. On the S side is a sumptuous sedilia, on the N side an Easter sepulchre more glorious than any in England. The sleeping soldiers crouch in the niches of the base; in the sepulchre itself the figure of Our Lord rising from the tomb stands with right arm raised, the grave clothes hanging from his shoulder—the three Marys with their offerings to the right, the niche for the Blessed Sacrament to the left. Above, amid a wealth of crockets, finials and foliage, the apostles gaze up at the feet of the Ascending Christ. Adjacent to the sepulchre is the tomb of the founder, Sir Robert

Hawksworth

Hawksworth

Compton (1330). Thomas Wotton (1741) tells us that in 1482 Sir Thomas Molyneux returned from an expedition into Scotland with Richard Duke of Gloucester, 'and in the same year he built the church, and a fair house, at Hawton'; this dates the tower, and the nave clerestory. The Molyneux tombs which Wotton described have disappeared; there are a few later monuments to the Holdens (of Nuthall Temple, q.v.). And no trace remains of the 'fair house': the Molyneux family acquired Teversal (q.v.) in the 17th century, and moved there. The moated site was used by the Parliamentary Army to build fortifications for the Siege of Newark in 1645, and the earthworks are still visible close to the river.

Hayton [5] At Clarborough the main road to Gainsborough turns right and makes for Wheatley: the minor road to Clayworth leads straight on; Hayton is more or less contiguous. A farmhouse with square, gabled 17th-century dovecote and grand farm buildings *en suite* stands on the left: a suburban development accompanies a side lane a little farther on, and leads to the *Church*. A narrow tower with ogee-topped windows; handsome pinnacled Perp porch; an interior with richly coloured Victorian glass and poppyheaded box pews; an EE S arcade with one foliated capital. The lane leads on to a bridge over the Chesterfield Canal, and peters out; at the E end of the church a rose-coloured Georgian (former) vicarage is embowered in cedars; and away to the NE on the rising ground in the Wheatley Hills a farmhouse called Hayton Castle occupies the site of the medieval castle of the de Haytons and Hartshornes.

Headon [5] Remote undulating country, SE of Retford. Driving along the quiet lane from Grove, the squat tower of the *Church* comes in sight, standing on its low escarpment—and the remains of an ancient avenue of venerable lime trees marches across a field from a wooden gate into the heart of a thick wood. Here stood the great house of the Wasteneys, baronets extinct. The lane leads on to a little village. Like its tower, the nave of the church is wide and low, with a flat ceiling to nave and chancel, but light with clear glass in aisles and clerestory. EE arcades; Jacobean pulpit; much grained panelling: an inscription on the Calvary in the N aisle records that the crown of thorns was gathered in Jerusalem, close to the site of the Judgment Hall, in the spring of 1907. The chancel is raised: in the floor are inscriptions to the Wasteneys, some broken or half concealed: '. . . the bodye of Sir Edmund Wasteneys, Baronet, who died March 12th 1678, and of the Lady Catherine his wife . . .'; 'Here lieth the body of Sir Hardolph Wasteneys, Bart, who departed this life . . .' On the wall is a solitary tablet to the last baronet: 'Here lie the remains of Sir Hardolph Wasteneys, Bart. Being the last of his family in the male line, Who how respectable soever for the antiquity of it was more so for the excellency of his virtues . . . died December 17th 1742'. Headon passed to a great niece, who married Anthony Eyre of Grove, and the great house, designed by Sir Thomas Hewitt of Shireoaks, Surveyor General to the Office of Works, in 1710, was pulled down soon after.

Hickling [14] The Vale of Belvoir: good red-brick houses and cottages set in unfrequented undulating countryside on the Leicestershire border. The Grantham Canal calls here on its meandering overgrown course: 'Hickling Basin' is close to the *Church*. A church of great charm, too: a wide nave with old flat roof and square-headed clerestory windows, a long chancel sympathetically rebuilt in the early 19th century with Gothick reredos and gaudy E window, incorporating many fragments of ancient glass (inscribed 'Gul Mandell propraes 1839. Quod vult Deus volo'), some old benches with poppyheads, a 17th-century font cover, an early 19th-century organ, a 13th-century S door with original ironwork, a Saxon tomb cover with floriated carving, and a small brass in the chancel to Ralph Babington, Rector of Hickling, in eucharistic vestments (1521): 'calicem salutatis accipiam, et Nomen Domini invocabo' reads the inscription; he was son of Thomas Babington of Dethick, Derbyshire. A charming oddity is the old framed notice in the porch entitled 'Ye altar flowers', with spaces for names in what appears to be an early 19th-century engraving of Henry VII's Chapel. The churchyard filled with old slate headstones is redolent of the district.

High Marnham, *see* Marnham, High

Hockerton [11] Perfect, simple, little aisleless *Church*, with 14th-century embattled tower, one tiny Norman window in the nave, and early unmoulded round arch into the chancel. Victorian pine seating in the nave, with benchends copied from 16th-century original, copied in oak for chancel stalls. Indecipherable medieval inscription and fragment of Easter sepulchre in the sanctuary recess; little marble monument near by, with nonchalantly-draped urn, to the memory of John Whetham Esqre of Kirklington 'this marble urn erected, 1781'; also an oval, marble tablet set into the wall below, to John Augustine Finch, rector, 1780, with beautiful bold lettering. Ancient yew in churchyard. Handsome 18th-century brick farm buildings form courtyard to the *Manor*, which has blue diapering and little round windows around the original front door, 16th- or early 17th-century brickwork, and much old timber within; a house of great charm. Views across meadows towards Southwell.

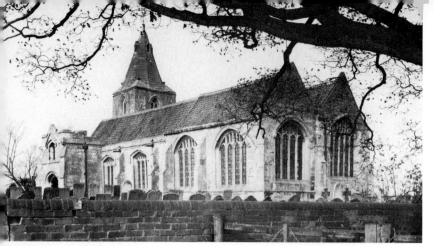

Holme-by-Newark

worshippers; there is a great array of ancient woodwork: rood screen with restored Calvary and attendant figures, Jacobean pulpit, stalls in the chancel and S chapel, 17th-century altar rails. The E end glows with richly furnished altar and medieval glass. The church was rebuilt by John Barton, and his tomb stands in the sanctuary; the S chapel is adorned with canopied stone niches, original stone altar, and elaborately carved stalls. It is a church which was forgotten not only by the Victorians, but also by the Georgians; marooned on the E side of the Trent when the river changed its course in the 17th century, Holme slumbered until the 1930s, when it was rescued by a devout layman, Nevil Truman, and his sympathetic architect, R. Harley Smith. The medieval glass was carefully reassembled, and fragments from Annesley, Salisbury and Beauvais added. 'Pray for the soul of John Barton of Holme, Merchant of the Staple of Calais, builder of this church, who died 1491, and for Isabella his wife. The fragments of his glass in the three centre lights were reconstructed by Nevil Truman of Nottingham, 1933'—so reads Nevil Truman's inscription. It is said that in Barton's house (which disappeared in the early 19th century) another window was inscribed: 'I thanke God, and ever shall/It is the sheepe hath payed for all'. The sheep still graze quietly in the lonely holms and carrs of the River Trent.

Holbeck [8] At the gates of Welbeck: a little *estate village* meticulously tended, and a small *Church* by Louis Ambler (1913) in Norman style, beautifully furnished and filled with *objets d'art*, the shrine of the Portland family. The churchyard is immaculate, with the tombs of recent dukes and other members of the family: of special interest are the graves of Lady Ottoline (1938) and her husband Philip Morrell (1943), with their plain stones handsomely carved by Eric Gill.

Holme-by-Newark [9] Two dead-end lanes, one from Winthorpe, one from Langford, lead to this tiny, solitary hamlet standing close to the E bank of the Trent, haunted by river birds and weekend fishermen. The medieval *Church* is perfection: low EE broach spire, broad Perp windows, grand two-storeyed Perp porch adorned with the arms of John Barton, Merchant of the Staple of Calais, pantiled roof. Inside, the orderly rows of poppyhead pews give the impression of kneeling

Holme Pierrepont [14] From the dual carriageway of the A52 it is possible to catch a glimpse, half screened by trees, of a venerable red-brick castellated house, with a church beside it, standing some distance away across the meadows. Radcliffe-on-Trent, the suburbs of Nottingham, the enormous new Regatta Course, all are near neighbours, and it is a long drive round to reach the historic house and its church, standing with a mere handful of cottages in remark-

Holme-by-Newark

able seclusion. *Holme Pierrepont* is the ancient home of the Pierrepont family, Earls and Dukes of Kingston, and Earls Manvers: through the failure of male heirs all these titles have become extinct; and Thoresby became the principal seat of the family in the 17th century. But Sir Henry Pierrepont married Annora de Manvers, heiress of Holme, in the 13th century. Holme has always belonged to the family, and still belongs today to descendants of its original builder, and in recent years has been restored with incredible skill and sympathy and brought back to life; 19th-century stucco has been stripped off the S and E fronts, revealing

the Tudor brickwork, a long garden has been created on the E, old rooms inside have been wonderfully re-created. The S front with its castellated towers and central archway is the gatehouse front of what was a great quadrangular mansion. Thoroton's view (1676) shows a tall, gabled range rising behind this front, which seems to have been pulled down when the family moved to Thoresby; early in the 19th century a new lower range was built on the N, and the whole house was then stuccoed. Over the years the house was intermittently occupied by a dowager, or an elder son, but was frequently deserted by the family. The S front contains the

lodgings, remarkably well preserved (and now restored), and a grand *Great Chamber* on the first floor with remarkable open roof; the E front contained the *Long Gallery*, and this is now being restored; there is also a magnifical Caroline staircase, with carved scrolled banisters; the courtyard is an enchanted parterre garden, and across the W wall is a view of the E end of the church. The great feature of the *Church* is the 17th-century S aisle, with classical porch and 'Gothic Survival' traceried windows—rather like 17th-century Gothic in Oxford: this contains the family tombs. The rest of the church is 13th century, with a Perp tower and spire; the chancel was rebuilt by Hine in 1878. There is a resplendent set of memorials to the Pierreponts: early effigies of the 13th and 14th centuries, and a splendid tomb (designed by John Smythson) to Sir Henry (1615), who married Bess of Hardwick's daughter. There are later monuments, to the last Duke of Kingston (1806), by Taylor of York, another, by Flaxman, to the Hon Evelyn Pierrepont; and of special charm is the small tablet to John Oldham, the poet (1686), a protégé of the 1st Earl of Kingston, in a spandrel of the arcade, adorned with garlands and swags and cherubs à la Grinling Gibbons. The house is open to the public regularly during the summer, and concerts are held in the Long Gallery. The great new *Regatta Course* was formed between 1969 and 1973 by the County Council and the Sports Council out of old gravel pits: it has been beautifully landscaped. National and international events are held here and it has brought new fame to Holme Pierrepont.

Hoveringham [11] The little red-brick Victorian *Church* (1865 by William Knight) looks ordinary enough, but, inside, is revealed a simple, small Victorian church at its very best, with plastered walls, red-brick quoins and 'varnished pitch pine', all immaculately kept

Holme Pierrepont

and cherished. Moreover, from the old church, it contains a notable Norman tympanum, of St Michael defending the Agnus Dei from two dragons; an unusual little Norman font; and the early 14th-century alabaster tomb of Sir Robert Goushill, with his wife Elizabeth Fitzalan; and there is a Victorian monument to General Huthwaite of the Bengal Army. Hoveringham Hall, once the home of the General, is a three-storeyed early 19th-century house with overhanging eaves and sash windows, protected by high garden walls. A lane leads down to the *Elm Tree Inn* on the river bank, and runs for a considerable distance along the Trent, commanding long views up- and downstream. The tower of Kneeton church peers over the hilltop on the opposite bank. The Hoveringham gravel pits are N of the village.

Hucknall [10] has became famous as the burial place of Byron: in itself it is a rather drab little town, surrounded by collieries, submerged by suburbia. The main square is little more than a car park, with Byron's figure prominent on the front of the Coop, but the parish church with its large churchyard is here. Much of the church is Victorian: as the town grew in the 19th century, so did the *Church*. The tower is 12th century, with a 14th-century top; the N arcade is 13th century; the chancel was rebuilt and what must be the longest transepts in the world were built by R.C. Clarke in 1887. The timber porch is 14th century, but there has been much renewal of the timber; there are 25 windows by Kempe. But the *Byron memorials* are the thing. In the sanctuary is a 17th-century monument to the 2nd Lord, describing how he 'with the rest of his family being seven brothers' faithfully served Charles I in the Civil War, and lost all their possessions, 'yet it pleased God to bless the honest endeavour of the said Richard Lord Byron that he repurchased part of their ancient inheritance . . .' He died in 1679, and was the brother of the 1st Lord, who had been made a peer in 1643 as a reward for his loyalty to the king. In the floor of the chancel is a marble slab: 'BYRON, born January 22 1788, died April 19th 1824'—with a laurel branch to adorn it. It was the gift of the King of the Hellenes in 1881. On the chancel wall above is a tablet with his head in profile, and the inscription: 'In the vault beneath (where many of his ancestors and his mother are buried) lie the remains of George Gordon Noel Byron, Lord Byron of Rochdale in the County of Lancaster, the author of Childe Harold's Pilgrimage. He was born in London on the 22nd January 1788. He died at Missolonghi in Western Greece on the 19th April 1824, engaged in the glorious attempt to restore that country to her ancient freedom and renown. His sister, the Hon Augusta Mary Leigh placed this tablet to his memory.' The Abbey would not have him, but Hucknall is proud to honour him.

Kelham [12] appears like a wondrous apparition on the banks of the Trent: St Pancras Station, suddenly, mysteriously, transplanted into Nottinghamshire? Red-brick towers, pinnacles, chimneys, gables,

Holme Pierrepont

Gothic windows—glistening in the sunlight, or frowning against a heavy sky—appear and disappear through the trees along the river bank, unmistakably declaring the hand of Sir George Gilbert Scott. *Kelham* was built between 1859 and 1862: St Pancras Station was begun a few years later, so there is indeed a close relationship. The name Kelham, however, became famous throughout the world in later years because of the Kelham Fathers (Society of the Sacred Mission), who acquired the house in 1903 as their Mother House, and here established a famous Anglican theological college. Indeed many people assumed that the house was built for a religious community. The odd thing is that it was built neither as a seminary nor as a rail-

way station, but as a private house—for John Manners-Sutton, whose family had lived here for centuries. The Suttons had acquired Averham, next door, by marriage with the de Lexingtons, who took their name from Lexington (or Laxton), and later added Kelham to their holding; they had a house here as well as at Averham when Charles I gave himself up to the Scots army, encamped at Kelham, in May 1646. Robert Sutton, 1st Lord Lexington, was the great defender of Newark in the Civil War: the second peer had no male heir and his daughter married the 3rd Duke of Rutland. It was the descendants of younger sons of the duke who inherited Kelham, and became Manners-Sutton: in course of time they produced an Archbishop of Canterbury, a Speaker of the House of Commons, and a Lord Chancellor of Ireland. John Manners-Sutton, who built the present house, was MP for Newark. The 18th-century house (by John Sanderson, 1728) was burnt down in 1857. The exterior of the house is a romantic essay in Florentine Gothic, built of bright red brick with stone dressings: from a distance the skyline seen across the meadows—from the railway or the Great North Road—is remarkable. Inside, spacious vaulted corridors run from end to end on all three floors: a great vaulted *Music Hall* is the grandest room, with a cathedral-like arcade with triforium opening into the ground and first floor corridors; beyond is a vaulted *Drawing Room*. Elaborately and wonderfully-carved capitals adorn the clustered columns, and the vaults are painted and gilded. Unfortunately the money ran out, various details were never completed, and the estate was sold in 1898. The Society of the Sacred Mission had been founded in Kennington, and when they came to Kelham in 1903 they established the theological college, which accepted young men at 16 or 17, and provided their schooling and then their theological education free of charge. It was a noble scheme, and many hundreds of Kelham priests have served the Anglican Church throughout the world. The Society built a domestic quadrangle for the college in the 1920s in dark red brick. To the N of the house they built their remarkable *Chapel* in 1929 (C.C. Thompson of Derby, architect). Domed, and in the Byzantine style, it is one of the great churches of the 20th century: the interior was dark, solemn and numinous; a great rood arch separated the dome from the apsidal sanctuary, and on this stood Sargent Jagger's Rood; three sanctuary lamps burned in front of the altar; there was a remarkable interplay of light and shade; it was a church that brought you to your knees. In 1969, for some incompre-

hensible reason, it was decided that the Church of England needed only one monastic theological college: Mirfield was chosen and Kelham closed its doors. The Fathers moved their Mother House to Milton Keynes, and the local District Council took over Kelham as offices. It is, of course, good that a use has been found for this great building: it is appreciated by its new owners, and excellently maintained. But it is sad that a house which once echoed to the sound of prayer and plainsong should now only echo to the sound of the typewriter. The chapel has been renamed the Dome and is used for bingo and dances, the cross removed from its top. Desecration. Near by stands the village *Church*, a perfect small late Perp building, all built at the same time, embattled, pinnacled, clerestoried, with a beautifully proportioned interior. It is a surprise, and a pleasure, passing through the 15th-century choir screen, to discover a small Vanbrughian mausoleum grafted on to the S side of the chancel, and there the splendid baroque tomb of the 2nd Lord Lexington (1723) and his wife; there are one or two other monuments and much else of interest. Near the N porch is a very different memorial, the grave of a Kelham student who died here at the age of 17. And to the S of the churchyard, in its own secluded garden, is the burial place of the monks—with rows of identical headstones recording the date and age of each member, and the years of his profession.

Kersall [8] A lane leads off the main road from Newark to Ollerton (A616) and descends steeply into a little valley watered by the beck. A cluster of old brick cottages, a farm, no church; that is all there is of Kersall. Undiscovered Nottinghamshire at its prettiest best.

Keyworth [14] Commuterland. Within the last 50 years Keyworth has grown enormously; rows and

rows of 'desirable residences' now climb the slopes of the wolds and the centre of the village is now anonymous with supermarkets and other shops. One thing, however, is unique: the *church tower*, of which there is no exact parallel in England. Built in the 15th century, this tall, buttressed tower, with its unusual grouping of Perp windows, is crowned by a plain parapet: recessed behind that rises an octagonal embattled stone lantern with square-headed windows, which in its turn is crowned by a short spire. The rest of the *Church* is 14th century, and delightfully furnished. The *reredos* to the High Altar, by T.N. Lawson, is brilliant and effective; the date, *incredibile dictu*, is 1963—just when the stark stumpy style of the Liturgical Movement became *de rigueur*. A devout and beautiful interior.

Kilvington [12] The little River Devon and watery meadows separate Kilvington from Staunton: an early 19th-century former rectory, a farmhouse or two, and a couple of cottages accompany the little church standing on its low hill surveying the Vale of Belvoir. There is a grand view of the Castle, with the needle spire of Bottesford in the foreground. A goods line passes by. The *Church* with low pyramid tower was rebuilt in 1852: it is the perfect little Victorian village church, with varnished pews and plastered walls: 'Praise God in his sanctuary' proclaims a painted text over the tower arch; 'Give ear, O Lord, unto my prayer' another over the chancel arch. And there is richly jewelled Victorian glass in the chancel windows.

Kimberley [10] The suburbia of Nuthall carries on: the road to Eastwood dives through the narrow street of Kimberley with its shops, 19th-century housing and old industry. There is a small *Church* of 1847, with bellcote and apsidal chancel; but the biggest and most conspicuous building is the brewery: Hardy's Kimberley Ales.

Kelham

Kingston-on-Soar [13] An estate village, with groups of 19th-century red-brick cottages set around a green, a small church largely rebuilt in 1900, and a large but somewhat sombre Victorian–Elizabethan mansion set in a spacious park. It was Edward Strutt, 1st Lord Belper, grandson of Jedediah Strutt, who built the house (by Blore, 1842) and laid out the village, his son who rebuilt the *Church* (R. Creed, architect). Its tower and nave were designed to blend with the surviving fragments of the ancient chancel, and with the Babington Chantry. The interior is dominated by the chantry, erected by Anthony Babington in 1540, standing on the S side of the chancel. With its squat pillars patterned all over with carved lozenges, the immense projecting capitals adorned with the Babington rebus of babes in tuns, with its vaulted canopy and embattled and pinnacled top, it is an extraordinary composition, with few, if any, parallels in England. Sir Sacheverell Sitwell has likened it to a Portuguese–Indian temple: 'Persons familiar with Alcobaça or Belem will be unable to dismiss from their minds that there is somewhat of Portuguese–Indian influence in this church upon a tributary of the River Trent.'

Kinoulton [14] A long village street with many new villas and some older cottages and houses, and an unexpected 18th-century *Church* built in bright red brick with pyramid-crowned tower. 'This church was erected in 1793 by Henry Earl of Gainsborough' reads an inscription over the entrance; there is a W gallery, and a small organ in a contemporary Gothick case. The old church stood on the edge of the wolds, close to the Foss Way: the old churchyard survives, and on the way up may be seen another unexpected sight—a herd of highland cattle. The inn-sign on the *Nevile Arms* displays the arms of Nevile quartering those of Noel,

Earls of Gainsborough: the daughter of the builder of the church, the 4th Earl (of Exton, Rutland) married Christopher Nevile, of Wellingore, Lincolnshire. The Grantham Canal pursues its meandering overgrown course through the village, on its long inconsequential journey via half the villages of the Vale.

Kirkby-in-Ashfield [10] The Erewash Valley: a glance at the map tells all—'mine', 'works', 'mine (disused)', 'course of old railway', 'cemetery'. Vintage Erewash Valley. It is scarred countryside, and almost everything of antiquity has been destroyed, the few old cottages replaced by 'desirable' modern bungalows, the ancient church destroyed by fire in 1907. This was replaced, by a painstaking replica in sympathetic style by Louis Ambler; the tall broach spire is effective. At the E end stands the beautiful early 18th-century *Rectory* in its garden—now of course sold. To the S the road descends to the Bentinck colliery, and the earth opens up. It is scarred countryside indeed.

Kirklington [11] The tall 17th-century brick tower of the church is a commanding landmark as the road from Newark descends into the village; the base is medieval (with a stout S staircase), the crown Strawberry Hill Gothick. The church itself was much rebuilt in early or later 19th century: well-furnished interior, with one 17th-century monument in the sanctuary, and several 19th-century tablets to the Whethams in the chancel. There are several comely red-brick houses in the village, and a pretty little school of 1840. Kirklington Hall, once the seat of the Whethams, now the *Rodney School*, is in origin a handsome late 18th-century house, but in the early 20th century it was all stuccoed and Jacobethanized with an extraordinary result. The *park* is beauti-

ful: beech woods and plantations clothe the low hills; a grass drive climbs to a gate on the road to Hockerton, from where there is an unexpected view of Southwell.

Kirton [8] The lane from Egmanton passes through undulating country, and suddenly descends to Kirton: the village at the foot of the hill, the *Church* on the bluff above. A Perp tower, of the familiar Notts type, the rest of the church EE, with some Victorian restoration, but the charm of the church is the way its builders took advantage of the site: four steps lead up to the chancel on the higher ground, two more to the sanctuary, so the stone altar with its tabernacle and six candles is the focal point of the whole church; a few fragments remain of ancient glass, an immense Victorian pulpit, and many objects of piety—altogether a devout and prayerful church. There are wide views from the hillside—to Ollerton and its colliery to the S, to the woods of Clumber and Thoresby to the W, and to quiet pastoral country towards Haughton and Bothamsall to the N—and good brick houses in the village, notably the 17th-century *Hall Farm*, with its attendant buildings.

Kneesall [8] The A616 (Newark–Ollerton) climbs to Kneesall: the *Church* is upon us with its bold W tower and embattled and pinnacled Perp exterior, and spacious, if somewhat bare, interior, save for a few old benchends and the fragment of an Anglo-Saxon shaft. As the road descends again it passes the *Old Hall*, a rare early Tudor, brick hunting lodge, built by Sir John Hussey, 1st Lord Hussey, chief Butler of England, in the early 16th century. With its blocked-up archway, blocked-up windows, modern plate glass and incongruous slate roof, it is but a ghost of its former self: even now, its mellow red brick and terracotta details command attention, as the road sweeps through the village.

Langar

Kneeton [11] was originally spelt Kneveton, but of course always pronounced 'Kneeton', in good Notts fashion. The dramatic view from the churchyard down the steep hillside to the Trent is always a surprise, especially after driving across the (apparently flat) Vale of Belvoir. A cluster of good farm houses and old barns and buildings round the church; pretty cottages comprise the rest of the small village. The *Church* was much rebuilt by Ewan Christian towards the end of the 19th century, but is attractive in a simple way; gloomy plain glass. Under the tower are a few elegant marble tablets, three little ones looking like oblong china plates. The tower is Perp.

Lambley [11] survives as a village, despite the proximity of Nottingham suburbs, of Gedling colliery and Burton Joyce; Lambley sits in an undulating valley, watered by the Cocker brook. There are some older houses and many new villas. The *Church* is distinguished, all of one date except for the earlier tower, and built by Ralph Lord Cromwell, Lord High Treasurer of England, builder of Tattershall Castle in Lincs, and Wingfield Manor in Derbs (*see* Cromwell); Lambley was his birthplace. It is an imposing Perp 'hall' church, with nave and chancel lit by great tall windows, and no side aisles. The Lord Treasurer's badge—a purse—adorns the E wall; 14th-century screen; Jacobean pulpit; 17th-century altar rails; some fragments of ancient glass.

Laneham [9] Here the Trent makes a great sweep, and there are views up- and downstream, with small craft moored along the bank. Cottam power station is a dominating presence to the N, High Marnham a more distant presence to the S. Flat desolate countryside. The long village street, with several good-looking houses, leads to the river, the *Church* standing gaunt and ancient on the bank. Plain W tower; much Norman work, much herringbone masonry, with an enormous buttress supporting the S wall of the nave; rare (for Notts) 14th-century timber porch, sympathetically restored in 1932; an ancient door with early ironwork. The interior is scraped, but full of interest; 13th-century N arcade, Norman font, 17th-century pulpit, 17th-century pews, an enormous 13th-century chest, a fragment of 14th-century glass. In the chancel, marble tomb to Ellis Markham 'Justice of Peace in ye countie of Nottingham' and his son Gervase 'Captain of ye Horse in ye sayde countie who long served Her Majestie in her warres with extraordinary proof in Ireland and ye Lowe Countries': the two figures kneel, one behind the other, between Corinthian columns, under a pediment adorned with garlands; the date is 1636, and it is an accomplished work, sophisticated and urbane—surprising to find here in remote Laneham, but the Markhams were an accomplished family (*see* East Markham). All trace of their mansion, which stood close to the river, has long since vanished.

Langar [14] The *Vale of Belvoir*, at its widest and its best. From the S a long lime avenue leads up to Langar Hall; nearer the church old brick walls and blocked-up, mutilated, gatepiers suggest a vanished layout, a vanished magnificence; at the E end of the church bold 18th-century piers, capped with balls, guard the entrance to the house. Close by, the gracious early 18th-century *Old Rectory*, with its sash windows and hipped roof, was the birthplace of Samuel Butler, whose father was rector here. There are pretty cottages, one or two larger houses, and the *Unicorn's Head* (1717): altogether a delectable ensemble. The *Church* was much restored by the Revd Thomas Butler in the 1860s, but the interior has the air of ancient charm: a large cruciform church, with EE arches at the crossing, and

later 13th-century arcades in the nave, a Jacobean pulpit, and 17th-century altar rails. But the monuments are the thing. In the N transept are the tombs of the Chaworths of Wiverton: the earliest is of George Chaworth 'late Lord of Wereton and Annesley ... for whose soul of your charitie say a Pater Noster and Ave Marie'; he died in 1521. His son, Sir John Chaworth and his wife lie near by (1558), likewise his grandson, Sir George (1587). And there are later Chaworth-Musters tablets. In the S transept are the Scropes, who inherited Langar from the Tiptofts, and their successors, the Howes: the great four-poster tomb of Thomas Lord Scrope (1609) is of the most accomplished work; two elegant busts on tapered pedestals stand behind, to Scrope, 1st Viscount Howe (1712), and Scrope, 2nd Viscount (1734); and on the W wall a tablet commemorates Langar's greatest son, Richard, 3rd Viscount and 1st Earl Howe, the Admiral (1799),

victor of the Glorious First of June (1794). The Glorious First of June is always celebrated at Langar. The extraordinary raised platform in the S aisle is the Howe family vault. An old picture shows *Langar Hall* as a tall Elizabethan house: this was subsequently Georgianized and a great pedimented portico added to the W front. After the Admiral's death the property descended to his daughter, who became Baroness Howe of Langar and married the Hon Penn Assheton Curzon, of Penn (Bucks): her son was created Earl Howe (of the second creation), and the present Lord Howe is his descendant. Langar Hall was sold in 1818; the great house was pulled down, and the present house built, in 1837, incorporating a small wing of the old mansion. A house of special charm, with sash windows and hipped roof, stuccoed and apricot washed, it stands on an elevated site surveying the Vale and the ancient trees in the park. The property was sold twice in the 19th century, and

descended to the late Geoffrey Huskinson, the county cricketer and president of Notts County Cricket Club, who did so much to lay out and replant the rare *garden* in the valley below the house. Here medieval fishponds, later canalized (perhaps by Stephen Switzer, who was a friend of the Howes) were romantically planted, and the hanging gardens formed by Mr Huskinson, who spoke of 'urning his living' in the gardens at Langar. This aura pervades them today. *Wiverton* (pronounced Werton) is a short distance to the N. The medieval hamlet disappeared long ago, but the great Tudor gatehouse to the ancient Chaworth mansion survives, and on to this an enchanting new house in Strawberry Hill Gothick was built in the early 19th century. The old house was largely destroyed in the Civil War: Annesley (q.v.) became the Chaworths' principal seat, but Wiverton remained their property till recent times.

opposite and above, The Stables and the walled garden at **Langold**

Langford [12] The church stands in blissful isolation down the dead-end lane which leads to Holme and the Trent. Near by runs the modest stream called the Fleet, which marks the old course of the Trent, and the railway line to Lincoln. A pretty *Church*, with 13th-century tower and red pantiled roof, blocked N arcade and clerestoried nave well-furnished with 19th-century poppyhead pews; there is a late 14th-century effigy, and an early 19th-century tablet to Slingsby Duncombe in the chancel. To the S stands the *Old Hall*, a romantic 16th-century stone fragment, with prominent porch and blocked-up mullioned windows, surrounded by farm buildings. The village lies astride the Gainsborough road: three good-looking long low farmhouses of stone and brick face the road; and, nearer the Foss, and surrounded by its park and plantations, stands *Langford Hall*, a tall, distinguished house of red brick with stone adornments, with central pediment and Roman Doric porch, built at the very end of the 18th century for the Duncombes, by John Carr of York.

Langold [5] The colliery village on the main road (A60) is unpromising, but a lane to the W leads down to Langold Lake—formed in the early 19th century by that accomplished man, Henry Gally Knight (*see* Warsop and Southwell), in preparation for the building of a castellated house designed in 1814 by Sir Jeffry Wyatville. The house was never built, but the landscaped setting gives some clue to what was envisaged. The words 'Langold Farm' on the map, a little way to the W and right on the Yorkshire border, do not prepare one for the buildings which were erected here by his father, Ralph Gally Knight, and which indeed still stand, used as a farm: great brick walls enclosing the kitchen garden; magnifical stables looking like buildings in a Piranesi print; and a little garden pavilion with pedimented front and

spreading roof à la James Paine—if not by Paine, perhaps designed in his style by Ralph himself, a gifted amateur of architecture. The garden pavilion is now the farmhouse, the stables farm buildings; they stand a stone's throw into the West Riding, but are spiritually and dynastically so closely connected with Nottinghamshire that they must be included here. And close to Langold village, on the main road, stand the magnificent stone quadrangular farm buildings of Hodsock Grange, perhaps the most splendid farm buildings in the country.

Laxton [8] is celebrated because here, and here only, has the medieval system of Open Field farming continued until today. Why it has continued, and how it has continued, is a mystery. Laxton, therefore, is different: approaching it from Kneesall, or Ollerton or Ossington the great Open Fields—the South Field, the West Field, the Mill Field, the East Field—great rolling tracts of land cultivated in long narrow strips, will be clearly seen. On arriving in the village it will be noted that the farms and their great buildings are all adjacent to the street—not scattered across the countryside as elsewhere. It is a pleasure, and of great interest, to walk up the open roads or rather open tracks of (let us say) the South Field, and survey the scene from the top—the different strips of land cultivated by different hands in different ways for different crops, the divisions carefully marked by pegs or sikes. The administration is in the hands of the Court Baron, which meets every year, summoned by the bailiff, presided over by the steward; each year the jury and the pinder are appointed—the jury to see that the ditches are clearly defined and marked out, the pinder to impound straying beasts in the pinfold, and locate the owners. The Court meets at the Dovecote Inn, at the top of the street. As always in Notts the

farmhouses and buildings are very fine, and Laxton is a village of warm red brick. On the high ground to the N is the great mound of the *medieval castle*, the best preserved and largest motte and bailey in the county. To the W, in prominent position, and presiding over the village, is the *Church*. The Perp clerestory of the nave is notable, but until the restoration of 1860 the nave was one bay longer: the tower was therefore rebuilt further E, and given its Victorian pyramid top. Inside, the nave arcades are EE; the chancel is Dec, long and lofty, and on either side are the tombs of the de Everinghams, 14th-century lords of the manor. There is much good Dec detail in sedilia and Easter sepulchre, and the screens are of interest, especially that in the N aisle, dated 1532.

Leake, East [14] The coming of the Great Central Railway led to the building of prosperous Edwardian villas for Nottingham people; although the line is closed, there are hundreds of snug little suburban houses, and an enormous estate of pre-fabs climbs the hill towards Gotham. Little left of the old village except a few old houses near the church, the Baptist chapel (1829) and the stream running down the street. Important *Church*: Norman tower, with plain 15th-century spire; Norman nave with herringbone masonry and two small windows in N wall—the S aisle and clerestory added in early 14th century. The Dec E window of the S aisle is notable; and inside there are early 17th-century pews, a 13th-century octagonal font, and a magnificent shawm, used to encourage the singing in church ('with trumpets also and shawms'). The propeller fans rotating in the roof are an unexpected feature.

Leake, West [13] 'Hanc aedem vetustate collapsam refecit et ornavit Edwardus Baronius de Belper, 1876' reads a small brass plate near the S porch: the 1st Lord

Farm buildings at Hodstock Grange near **Langold** ▷

Children's amusement park near **Cottam** power station

Belper (of Kingston Hall) indeed restored this ancient *Church*, rebuilt the clerestory and gave it its high-pitched roof and lofty bellcote. His architect was Henry Hall. But the blocked Norman doorway and little Norman window in the N wall proclaim its antiquity. Long nave with 14th-century S arcade; behind the organ two early effigies, one with head under elaborate canopy (13th century); elsewhere a number of tablets to former rectors and several monuments to the Mansfield family—the bust of Thomas Mansfield surveys the sanctuary (1743). Delectable setting: great trees adorn the little green by the church; great drifts of snowdrops in early spring adorn the churchyard, which slopes gently to the brook, and to undulating country beyond. W of the church the Old Rectory, with Georgian windows masking an older house; a quiet village street of old brick cottages and farms.

Leverton, North and South [6] In remote, flat, power station country, close to the Trent. It is all sky, with

the enormous power stations of West Burton and Cottam standing like great pagan temples close to the river: the rites are for ever being performed, and the steam from the sacrifices goes up day and night. North Leverton is flatter, more exposed: there is a *windmill*, the only working windmill in the county, still grinding corn; at the crossroads in the middle of the village are some of the finest *farm buildings* in the county, forming an early 19th-century brick quadrangle of barns, buildings and dovecote adjoining the house. The *Church* has a plain embattled Perp tower; the steep gables of nave, lofty chancel, and short, lofty S aisle group attractively against it, and inside light pours in through traceried Dec windows on to a spacious panelled interior. There is a smudge of drab, dreary, modern terrace houses along the road to South Leverton—a subtopian intrusion. South Leverton is remarkable for many handsome brick buildings—a late 17th-century *dovecote* with stepped gables, a slightly faded house op-

posite the church with pedimented door (the old school) and, farther down the street, a Dutch gable (but, alas, ruined by terrible modern fenestration). The *Church* has a Norman tower, exceptional EE nave arcades with foliated capitals, and much geometrical tracery; the chancel, restored by Ewan Christian, is dark with Victorian glass.

Linby [11] An unexpected, pretty stone-built village, with a stream running down the street, two village crosses (one medieval and 19th century, one 17th century), a church with a Nottinghamshire square tower, and two notable houses: the Hall, and Castle Mill. The *Church* has a distinguished Perp porch and a terribly scraped, snail-pointed interior. The best thing is the monument to William Sedden, a former rector, 'who at the sight of the Anglican Church gasping for breath, himself became breathless, and rendered up his life to God through Christ. 28 February 1684'. His example might be fol-

North Leverton Mill:
working and at rest

lowed by a few sensitive clergymen today. *Linby Hall*, despite its long rows of 17th- or early 18th-century windows, looks medieval, and is. It is the romantic fragment of a large and ancient manor house, perhaps originally containing the long gallery: little octagonal staircase turrets survive at each end. A dovecote on one side, a brewhouse on the other, complete the delectable composition; in the farm buildings is an old millwheel. *Castle Mill* looks medieval, and isn't. It is a late Georgian Gothick water-mill, built by the Robinsons (*see* Widmerpool), with low, embattled towers at each end, now sympathetically converted into a house for himself by Mr Belleairs, the architect. On the garden side a long studio gallery looks on to a green garden, watered by the stream beneath the mill.

Littleborough [6] A wonderfully remote spot: a tiny hamlet detached from the world, detached from its neighbourhood, a mere handful of houses close to the river

Littleborough: toll house
and church

bank where the Trent makes its
slow, stately way through the flat
lands of northern Nottinghamshire,
and a tiny Norman church. Yet this
was in the remote past a place of importance, the Roman town of Se-
gelocum, where the Roman road,
the Till Bridge Lane, from Lincoln
to Doncaster crossed the river by
ford or ferry. The opposite bank is
Lincolnshire, with the well-wooded
park of Gate Burton—and its little
18th-century gazebo just visible in
the trees. There are tremendous
views upstream, as the river twists
and turns, to Cottam power station,
and High Marnham beyond that.
The *Church* is very simple: a Norman doorway, a double bellcote, a
Norman chancel arch, a little
organ, beautiful oak pews and
furnishings; the nave windows are
early 19th-century insertions, but
nothing can detract from the

ancient texture, the herringbone masonry, the Roman tiles. A holy spot. The straight Roman road still leads on in its purposeful way to Sturton-le-Steeple: at the junction with the lane to Cottam stands a little hexagonal *tollhouse*. Yet what traffic plies this lonely track today?

Lowdham [11] Ruined by the dual carriageway of the A6097 which, having crossed Gunthorpe Bridge, proceeds to charge relentlessly towards Ollerton and Doncaster. Along the road to Nottingham there are some small Victorian houses, and there is residential development everywhere, but a fragment of the old village survives to the NW of the new road, with the church and 17th-century timbered manor house, all prettily set. Imposing *Church* with late Norman tower crowned by 15th-century spire; spacious interior with lofty 13th-century nave (with Perp clerestory), and long, much-restored Dec chancel; fine 14th-century font; and effigy of Sir John de Lowdham in the chancel (1318).

Low Marnham, *see* Marnham, Low

Mansfield [7] Approaching Mansfield from the N or from the E the only prominent landmarks are the winding towers of local collieries: Forest Town, New Clipstone, Rainworth, Blidworth; the mining villages stand around. Beyond and below older industry and older housing occupy the view. To the W and to the S the hills are clothed with newer housing estates. In the town itself, some character is preserved from an earlier civilization, but the air of Victorian industry is dominant. There are few notable buildings, and a new inner relief road which encircles the centre of the town has torn apart the very bones of the place: dual carriageways and one-way streets with traffic rushing by, multi-storey car parks, shopping precincts, the inevitable supermarkets and all the

Mansfield

adjuncts of our decaying civilization, are bleak and grim. What gives the place immense character is the *railway viaduct*, carried on tremendous stone arches right through and above the centre of the town, high above houses, shops and factories. Built in 1875 of rough-hewn stone, here is a Piranesi print come to life in Nottinghamshire. Near by, the *Market Place* has some dignity with Lady Oxford's *Moot Hall* (1752), a handsome stone house with her arms and inscription in the pediment; in the centre of the Square—another link with Welbeck—is Hine's pinnacled monument to Lord George Bentinck (1849). The *Town Hall*, a classical building by W.A. Nicholson (1836), stands near by. From under the great viaduct, the medieval *Parish Church* can be seen, with its low spire and embattled exterior. The lower part of the tower

is Norman, the upper part Dec, and the spire itself (unexpectedly) of 1666: well-furnished interior, with early 14th-century arcades, and organ from Clare College, Cambridge. Round the church are a few 18th-century houses. *St John's* (to the NW) is a large Victorian church, prominent with its tall spire, designed by Stevens of Derby (1854), the gift of Henry Gally Knight (who gave the French glass for the E windows at Southwell); he himself had died in 1846. Perhaps the most notable church is *St Mark's* in Nottingham Road, a masterpiece by Temple Moore (1897). The exterior is dignified but plain, the interior original and moving. Like a great medieval 'hall' church, with no aisles proper, but with a narrow passage running under low arches in the wide square piers; all eyes are directed to the High Altar; the furnishings throughout are sensitive

and beautiful; it is a church with a powerful devotional atmosphere. There are one or two old houses near St Mark's, which look as though they had strayed from some old local village: farther along the Nottingham road there is attractive housing of the 1920s and early 30s, but acres of council houses accompany the high road to Sutton-in-Ashfield. However, there are wide views to open countryside, and here and there old *textile mills* in the valley below. It is industrialized countryside, full of atmosphere, and worth exploring.

Mansfield Woodhouse [8]An old settlement in Sherwood Forest. Now, of course, but part of the urban sprawl of Mansfield: old industrial buildings, newer industrial housing—all somewhat commonplace. But unexpectedly the nucleus of the old village survives: church,

△ **Mansfield Woodhouse**
◁ **East Markham**

Mattersey Priory

manor house, village street; and the group of *Manor House* and *Parish Church* is one of considerable charm. The house, no doubt of Tudor and 17th-century origins, stands Georgianized and castellated in a high walled garden; it is now council offices. Next door, the church has a dumpy 13th-century broach spire of unusual outline, with dormers near the base and tiny, pinnacled dormers very near the top, giving the effect of a little corona. The church was largely rebuilt in 1847 by Scott—one of his earliest commissions, and harmonious and attractive; 17th-century Digby monument, with standing figures of Sir John Digby and his wife (1684)—rather far north, it seems, for Digbys, from Rutland or the West Country, but they held the manor for a short time in the 17th century. There are several good stone 17th- or 18th-century houses in the village street.

Maplebeck [8] A hidden, secluded, tiny village embowered in great trees: narrow lanes from Kersall, from Winkburn, from Caunton, lead into its little valley, watered by the Beck. A few red-brick cottages, a farm or two, a church with a short broach spire, the minute *Beehive Inn*—all undiscovered, unsophisticated, charming. A tulip tree and ancient hollies adorn the churchyard slopes, and there is a great cedar in the rectory garden; the *Church* itself (13th and 14th century) was rescued from near-dereliction in 1898 by Hodgson Fowler. A porch with ancient timbers leads into an interior delightfully furnished with 17th-century pews, screen, altar rails, and a pulpit with a square, solid sounding board.

Markham, East [8] A great Perp church—a prominent landmark from the Great North Road, and from the main railway line to Scotland. The village stands in the gentle undulating country E of Tuxford, by-passed now by the A57, a large village of many lanes. The *Church* stands on its edge, overlooking open country, and as with the great Perp churches of East Anglia, it is a pleasure merely to walk round the outside, and catch glimpses of a spacious interior through great windows of clear glass. The interior will not disappoint: Comper's richly coloured High Altar, his richly lustrous E window (1896), the beautifully furnished chapels, lead the eye to the E end. Features include an early 17th-century pulpit; 17th-century altar rails guard the sanctuary; the whole church is beautifully and devoutly furnished. There is a pretty little chamber organ, a 17th-century font (on a medieval base), and the stone mensa in the N Chapel was discovered, face downwards, in the floor by a previous incumbent as the result of a dream. In the chancel stands the alabaster tomb of Sir John Markham, the judge (d.1409); in the Lady Chapel is the brass to his wife, Dame Millicent Mering (1419)—she subsequently married Sir William Mering. There are slabs in the sanctuary to the Williamsons, baronets (created 1642), who succeeded the Markhams here, but later migrated, by marriage, to Co. Durham. The great Notts family of Markham take their name from here: Sir John Markham drew up the instrument for the deposition of Richard III; his youngest son, also Sir John, was Lord Chief Justice and founded the Sedgebrook branch. The senior line moved later to Cotham (q.v.): descendants of younger sons founded the branches at Ollerton and Laneham (q.v.). Judges, knights, bishops, soldiers, politicians, priests and nuns appear in profusion in their pedigree, hanging in the chancel. The 17th-century brick manor house, W of the church, is supposed to occupy the site of their great house; the late 18th-century *Markham Hall*, with its three-storeyed pedimented front, was built by the Kirke family, who succeeded the Williamsons here. A stained glass window in the church commemorates Mrs Markham, author of *Mrs Markham's History of England* (1823); she was, in fact, Mrs Penrose, and daughter of Edward Cartwright of High Marnham (q.v.), but adopted the *nom de plume* of Markham from her birthplace here.

Markham, West [8] The signpost 'West Markham' stands on the Old North Road N of Tuxford. From the top of the hill there are splendid views, to the enormous power stations along the Trent to the E, and to East Markham Church closer at hand. The lane dips down to the tiny village of West

West Markham
church and font

The Newcastle Mausoleum, **Milton**

Markham (or Markham Clinton) —a mere scattering of cottages and farms, and a little *Church* with weather-boarded bell turret, which looks as though it had strayed from Surrey, from a well-wooded valley near Leith Hill. It is a little building of great charm, with Saxon masonry in the walls, and a Norman door; there is even the original Saxon mud floor (covered over at the E end of the nave, for convenience, but exposed at the back of the church). Old pews, a remarkable Norman font, a Jacobean pulpit, the skeleton of an ancient screen, a stone altar, 17th-century altar rails, an early effigy— these are the pleasures of this little unsophisticated church, which escaped the heavy hand of the Victorian restorers by being abandoned in favour of the new church and mausoleum at Milton (q.v.), built by the Duke of Newcastle in 1832. The little church was sympathetically restored before and after the Second World War, and is once again in use.

Marnham, Low and High [9] The quiet lane from Normanton leads towards the river, the great power station at High Marnham beckoning. The small village of Low Marnham comes first, sad and rather withdrawn—merely a few houses, and the church: two pinnacles have fallen off the tower, and the building itself is in poor repair and out of use. It must be hoped that rescue is at hand because it is of some distinction: an ogee S door leads into a spacious clerestoried nave, with an early 13th-century S arcade of detached shafts and foliated capitals, and a simpler and earlier N arcade; the chancel is EE, with chancel arch and arcade to N chapel akin to the S nave arcade; the exterior is embattled and Perp. There are two noteworthy late 17th-century monuments, one almost indecipherable, the other to Edward Nicholson, whose daughter married William Cartwright and brought Marnham to that interesting family. William's son, another William, is commemorated by a ledger stone in the chancel (1781), and was the father of three gifted brothers: George, ADC to the Marquis of Granby, who later spent 16 years as an explorer in Labrador; John, Parliamentary Reformer and agricultural innovator; and Edmund, Rector of Goadby Marwood (Leics), and inventor of the power loom and the wool-combing machine. The family (*see also* Ossington) sold Marnham at the end of the 18th century, and their great house (which stood between Low and High Marnham) was demolished. The lane leads on to High Marnham—up almost indiscernibly rising ground—passes *High Marnham Hall*, an engaging early 18th-century house, and descends again to the water front, where stands the *Brownlow Arms*, a charming white-washed 18th-century building (which commemorates the subsequent ownership of Marnham by the Brownlows—until the 1920s). Overshadowing all is the power station, opened in 1962; and there are *splendid views* up- and downstream and across to Clifton Church standing solitary on the opposite bank. An incomparable spot.

Mattersey [5] The descent from Gringley-on-the-Hill is full of pleasures: the Chesterfield Canal and the River Idle make their wandering way through the country below; at Drakeholes the *White Swan* with its Palladian façade is one of the 'improvements' of the architectural 'Mr Acklom of Wiseton (q.v.), as is Pusto Hill Farm on top of the hill a little farther on; and so we cross the river and enter Mattersey. There is a handful of cottages and larger houses, a public house, and the *Church*: a pinnacled Perp tower, 14th-century nave, and an earlier arcade between chancel and N chapel—with the letter 'A' carved on a pillar marking Mr Acklom's repairs in the 18th century—and a Victorian font with tall wooden cover. Behind the organ is the great surprise: two 14th-century carved

Misson

panels, one depicting St Martin and the beggar, the other St Helen discovering the cross—dug up under the chancel floor in the 18th century, and perhaps originally from the Priory, which was dedicated to St Helen. A bumpy, grass track leads E beyond the church to the *Priory*, one of the least visited of all monastic sites, close to the river: a farmhouse, and fragments of the monastic buildings set in green lawns, tended by the Dept of the Environment. The ground plan is exposed, and it is possible to get some idea of this small Gilbertine house, founded in 1185. To the S are the remains of the refectory range, the dorter and the kitchen, and to the N a fragment of the

church tower. The situation is a special pleasure, with the River Idle flowing by and views across the flat, lonely meadows and stumpy willows to Wiseton beyond.

Milton [8] An astonishing sight from the roundabout at Markham Moor: a large classical church, standing entirely on its own on the hill to the SW, approached by an avenue of Lombardy poplars. This is the *Newcastle Mausoleum*, erected by the 4th Duke in 1832 in memory of his wife, and designed by Sir Robert Smirke. With its long nave, transepts and chancel, and its tall octagonal central tower crowned with a dome, it looks like a big Commissioners' church in S

Newark

London, appropriate (if a little chilling) in Kennington, amazing in rural Notts. The nave was intended to be the parish church, to replace the old village church at West Markham (q.v.): it is entirely separate from the transepts and E arm, which were to be the burial place of the family, entered by a grand portico at the E end. It is, of course, magnificent, but never much loved by the parishioners, nor, it seems, by the family. The 7th Duke built the movingly beautiful Chapel at Clumber, and thither the monument to the Duchess (by Westmacott) has been moved: only the sad and solitary monument to

the Duke (1851) remains at Milton. In recent years the old church has been brought back into use; after being deserted for some years, the Mausoleum has been taken over by the Redundant Churches Fund and is well maintained.

Misson [2] A dead-end village in bleakest most northerly Notts: indeed it can only be approached from Yorkshire (via Bawtry) or Lincolnshire (via Haxey); the River Idle cuts it off from Notts. But it is an engaging little place of many lanes, many old brick cottages. Interesting Perp *Church*, all embattled without, with short nave, and

chancel with attendant chapels, and a typical pinnacled Notts tower; interior dark and mysterious, over-scraped but attractive with its very low N arcade, and 17th-century pulpit. Much Victorian glass. Opposite the church, *River Lane* leads down to the Idle, and it is possible to walk along the river bank, newly planted with trees. On the far side Barrier Bank separates the river from the Mother Drain: together they flow E to join the Trent at Misterton Soss. The lane E soon peters out: it is only possible to reach Misterton by water. The lane N makes its way through the carrs, accompanied by drains and dykes, and eventually reaches Haxey.

Misterton [2] The railway from Gainsborough to Doncaster, and a long industrial straggle with Victorian terraces and red-brick villas, accompany the main road (A161: Retford–Goole): the church stands in the centre of the old village, accompanied by older cottages and farms—some with fine buildings— and Nonconformist chapels. It is a strange part of the world. The *Church* has a stocky 13th-century broach spire (carefully rebuilt in 1847), and a Victorianized interior which retains many medieval features. The most distinguished feature is *John Piper's window* in the Lady chapel—a powerful design depicting the symbols of the Crucifixion, the hands and feet of Our Lord, and the Sacred Heart translucent against a background of dark blues and blacks. The Chesterfield Canal passes through the village on its way to join the Trent at West Stockwith: there is a delightful *walk along the towpath*, with barges tied up near the Anchor Inn; and the lane N leads to *Misterton Soss*, a collection of cottages standing between the Mother Drain and the River Idle, facing N across the river to the lonely carrs beyond. Close by, stand two pump houses with tall chimneys (one dated 1828), which originally housed beam engines; they are now overgrown and derelict. The cottages are occupied by one of the best known taxidermists in England. A haunting spot.

Moorhouse [8] The pretty lane from Ossington: woods, green fields, and North Park Farm—a charming, mellow 18th-century house with barns and farm buildings under its own roof. The hamlet of Moorhouse has red-brick cottages and another good farmhouse, with symmetrical buildings; the little church built by Henry Clutton for Speaker Denison in 1860 looks decidedly French, and sits in a field, licked and loved by cows.

Muskham, North and South [12] The towers of North and South Muskham are conspicuous landmarks across the flat meadows of the Trent, N of Newark, the two villages almost contiguous, separated by the railway and the new dual carriageway of the A1. A long pathway through the churchyard leads up to *North Muskham Church*: an impressive battlemented Perp exterior; the interior lofty, light and spacious, with daylight pouring in through the wide, late Perp windows. There is a 15th-century screen, a 17th-century pulpit—but the rest of the admirable fittings are by W.H. Wood (Hodgson Fowler's successor) *c.*1927: the canopy and rood, the W gallery and organ, Lady chapel, and high altar furnishings; the elaborate and beautiful aumbry is by F.E. Howard. All these give the church its powerful devotional atmosphere. Old glass in many windows with the Barton rebus denotes Barton patronage in the 15th century (*see* Holme-by-Newark). Close to the High Altar is a curious little low pyramid tomb: 'Heare lyth ye corp of John Smithe,/Meate for wormes to fede therewith' (1583); there is one small, late 17th-century tablet near by, and a number of well-lettered floor stones throughout the church. The Trent flows close to the E end of the church, and there are grand views up- and downstream and across to Holme on the opposite bank. Down a lane N of the church the *Muskham Ferry* marks the site of the old ferry. Opposite the church, the Old Hall is a late 17th-century brick house; the former vicarage is by G.E. Street (1863), and a still earlier vicarage has many pretty Gothick features. A housing estate occupies the site of the Grange, a handsome late 18th-century house: all that survives is a portion of the serpentine kitchen garden wall close to the new dual carriageway. *South Muskham Church* has the grander tower, with Perp top and little figure of St Wilfrid in the ogee spandrel of an upper window;

scraped interior, with many early features in the wide nave and long chancel; there are a few old poppyheads in the chancel, and a few early 19th-century monuments, but the interior is dominated by Victorian furnishings: pitch pine pews, pitch pine pulpit and organ. The railway thunders past close to the E end of the church, and the S porch commands a distant view of Newark spire.

Newark-on-Trent [12] The great spire of Newark stands like a sentinel guarding the important place where the Foss Way and the Great North Road meet, guarding the important crossing of the Trent, dominating the castle and the town, dominating the wide flat meadows which extend mile after mile along the river here. The great thing to do is to make one's way into the Market Place. From all directions narrow streets lined with Georgian (or earlier) houses lead here: Newark *Market Place* is one of the grandest in England, and to stand here, whether as sightseer or shopper, is an experience that never palls. On the W side is John Carr's *Town Hall* (1774), with its Doric columns supporting a central pediment, and framing a balustraded balcony on the *piano nobile* above the rusticated base; the figure of Justice, the lion and unicorn, a pair of urns, crown the top. Inside is a great assembly hall, with Corinthian columns screening apsidal ends, with elegant plaster ceiling, and busts of George III and the 4th Duke of Newcastle; there is a smaller council chamber, equally elegant. On the S side the *Clinton Arms* and the former *Saracen's Head* stand on open colonnades—two early 18th-century façades, the *Clinton Arms* specially decorative with pedimented windows and rusticated quoins: 'W.E. Gladstone addressed Newark electors from a window in this hotel when returned as Conservative M.P. in 1832' reads a plaque on the front. In the SE corner the *Old White Hart* is an incredibly

109

Newark market place

The Ossington Coffee Tavern, **Newark**

The Town Hall

preserved late 15th-century timber-framed building, with two rows of saints along the front—all recently restored and glowing with colour. On the N side the *Moot Hall* stands on another open colonnade; in fact it is a faithful reproduction (1967) of the original built in 1708 by John Holles, Duke of Newcastle (Lord of the Manor), whose gilded arms appear above. But this side, indeed the whole square, is dominated by the parish church, whose Perp clerestory windows appear behind or between or above the houses, the spire sailing over all. There are other good houses all around: Porter's grocery shop (where some of the finest Stilton cheese in England may be obtained) is a handsome, early 18th-century house with a fine doorway, standing at the corner of Bridge Street; here Byron's first poems were printed in 1806. Two admirable late Victorian banks— the Midland opposite Porter's, and the National Westminster on the corner of Stodman Street—are highly ornamental; near by is the 16th-century timber-framed Governor's House. Down Stodman Street, passing the plastered and timbered 16th-century *Woolpack Inn*, one is confronted in Castlegate by the former Corn Exchange (1847 by Henry Duesbury), now the Silverline Bingo Hall ('Think lucky and you'll be lucky' it proclaims). Castlegate is lined with big 18th-century houses and on the W side, on the river bank, stand the ruins of the Castle. *Newark Castle* was built in the early 12th century by Alexander, Bishop of Lincoln, to command this important crossing from northern England; the gatehouse faces N, and dates from this time; the river front, high above the Trent, is but a shell, slighted after the great siege during the Civil War, when Newark stood as a Royalist stronghold beset on all sides by Cromwell's troops. Bishop Burghersh and Bishop Rotherham carried on Alexander's work in the 14th and 15th centuries: it remains an impressive and awesome relic.

Newark Castle

On the farther side of the Trent bridge stands the *Ossington Coffee Tavern*, Newark's grandest Victorian building; designed by Sir Ernest George (1882), and built by Viscountess Ossington, widow of Speaker Denison (*see* Ossington), it was planned as a temperance hotel to wean the public away from the evils of strong drink to the virtues of coffee. The experiment failed: after serving as offices for many years, it has recently reopened as the Ossington Fish Restaurant. It is an altogether splendid building, with elaborate gables and chimneys, oriel windows and arcades, adorned with carved woodwork and ornate plasterwork. Here turn right up Kirkgate: notice the *King's Arms* with its gilded achievement in cast iron, the timber-framed house where Lady Leeke entertained Henrietta Maria during the siege, and the Florentine Gothic banking house (now part of

The Brewery in North Gate, **Newark**

the *Technical College*) with its ornate windows and tower (by Watson Fothergill, 1887)—and the church is upon us. But on approaching the W front, cast your eye left down *Wilson Street*, built in 1766 by Dr Wilson, vicar of Newark: now that the E side of the narrow street has been removed the long brick terrace with its end pavilions (and the surviving pavilions opposite) makes an attractive piece of Georgian townscape, with views across the churchyard. *Newark Church* is without question one of the greatest medieval parish churches in England: the soaring spire (237 ft high), such a prominent landmark across the surrounding countryside, the great Dec windows in the S aisle, the lofty Perp nave and chancel with their elegant arcades and wide clerestory windows, the Perp transepts with their great windows, the E chapels, the early 16th-century rood screen, the carved stalls and misericords in the choir, the chantry chapels, the medieval glass in the SE chapel, the crypt with its Treasury, the monuments, the brass to Alan Fleming, Comper's great reredos—there is a great deal to see. Entering at the W door, the lower stages of the tower are EE, the upper part and the spire are Dec, as is the S aisle. Nave, transepts and chancel were rebuilt in lofty, airy Perp, though at the crossing there survive the isolated pillars of the earlier Trans church; the crypt, too, is a survival of this period. Stand at the W end and the eye takes in the full vista of this magnificent building: through the screen (by Thomas Drawswerd, 1508) Comper's reredos glows and provides a wonderful splash of colour and warmth that radiates the whole church; awestruck, the pilgrim will make his way to this holiest place. On either side of the sanctuary are stone chantry chapels (early 16th century)—that to the right to Robert Markham, with its rare paintings of the Dance of Death, that to the left to Thomas Mering: here the Blessed Sacrament is reserved. The chapels in the retrochoir are richly furnished, and a stairway leads down to the crypt. Here is the Treasury containing a display of silver from all over the diocese; but pride of place belongs to the great set of altar plate given to the church by Frances Lady Leeke in 1708, the largest set belonging to any parish church in England. Frances Leeke, daughter of Sir William Thorold of Marston, was the wife of Sir Francis Leeke, one of the Royalist commanders during the siege: her father was Captain of Array in the Royalist Army. This bequest was her thankoffering for the end of the troubles. Close to the S door is the Font, with a 15th-century base, and a bowl of 1660: on an adjoining pillar an inscription reads as follows: 'This fonte was demolish by ye rebels May 9th 1646. Rebuilt by the charity of Nicholas Ridley 1660'. Close to the font is the monument to Anne Markham (1601), recently rescued from the derelict church at Cotham, through the piety of her descendants. Leaving the church by the S porch, and walking again through the Market Place into Bridge Street, notice the early 18th-century house in Appletongate which faces the Square—an important focal point—and turn left into *Appletongate*. There are more good 18th-century houses here, especially the former vicarage, and the former Magnus Grammar School, behind which stand the Tudor school buildings; here is the excellent *Newark Museum*, where a most interesting collection of local antiquities is preserved and where, under the present curator, an invaluable record of the historic buildings of the town is maintained. Next door is an entertaining building, the Palace Theatre, a 1930s descendant of the Brighton Pavilion. And beyond again is the *Friary*, a 17th-century house on the site of a medieval friary, the home after the Civil War of Sir Francis Leeke; the large gardens are public, the house now flats. Retracing our steps through Cartergate, we come to Beaumond Cross; opposite is the Castle Brewery (Hole's Newark Ales, now Courage's), with its French Renaissance *Clock Tower*; Victoria Street and Albert Street have still more Georgian and early Victorian houses and lead to the *Queen's Sconce*, a large, grassy, Civil

War Royalist bastion close to the River Devon—'perhaps the most impressive extant work of the kind in this country' (*Newark-on-Trent, The Civil War Siegeworks*, HMSO, 1964). Millgate has still more; indeed all the little streets here are worth exploring. Here it is possible to walk down to the river, explore the lock, and cross the narrow bridge. From the opposite bank is a rewarding view of the Castle. Retracing our steps S, along Lombard Street, and walking down the London Road we find an entirely different pleasure—an unexpected gathering of Edwardian houses, such as Nos. 20 and 22, the house called Abbeywood, the Lilley and Stone School, the Girls' High School, and (equally unexpected) the early 19th-century *Bowls Pavilion* ('Let no man be biassed' reads the inscription) surveying the Bowling Green behind all this. Further S again are charming early 19th-century terraces with verandas or balconies (No 39 was the birthplace of Sir William Nicholson the painter), and the procession of good-looking Victorian and Edwardian houses goes on. There are two railway stations: the Castle Station (Midland Railway) is early Victorian Italianate; several notable 18th-century houses (especially Handley House) line the street leading to Northgate Station (Great Northern), and the late Victorian or Edwardian Brewery buildings further along repay attention. There have been a few casualties, but Newark has preserved itself from the terrible post-war massacre that has occurred at poor Grantham, where street after street has been destroyed. Here wiser counsels have prevailed, and Newark must be congratulated. There are a very few blots, but mercifully the multi-storey car park and the new shopping precinct between Lombard Street and the Market Place are largely invisible and may be ignored. Newark remains one of the finest towns of its size in England.

Newstead [10] The W front of *Newstead Abbey* is memorable indeed: on the left is the W end of the monastic church, open to the sky, open to everything, but one of the most perfect 13th-century W fronts in England, and like a smaller version of Wells or Salisbury. The great W window is open now, but the figure of the Virgin still stands in the topmost gable, as does the figure of Our Lord seated, in the tympanum of the W door. Buttresses divide the façade into three, with delicate arcading adorning the ground floor and delicate canopied niches above it; a quatrefoil frieze and crocketed pinnacles crown the top. The Augustinian priory of Newstead was founded by Henry II *c*.1170; at the Dissolution Henry VIII sold the property to Sir John Byron, who pulled down the church, leaving only the W façade, the Prior's Lodgings, and Great Hall; and the buildings round the Cloisters he converted into a house. It remained Byron property until 1817 when the 6th Lord Byron, the poet, sold the place to his old Harrow friend Colonel Wildman; in 1860 it was purchased by Mr Webb, whose descendants owned it till Sir Julien Cahn bought it, and presented it to the City of Nottingham in 1931. It is beautifully maintained: many manuscripts, letters, books, pictures and personal relics of the poet have been bequeathed to the house since: it is a pleasure to visit the place and absorb its atmosphere. Standing before the W front one can see at a glance what has happened. Much of the fenestration is 19th century; the 'Norman' Sussex tower in the right-hand corner was built for Colonel Wildman by the architect John Shaw, and the long W wing, which looks so convincingly monastic, is also by him; 18th-century pictures show the entrance up a flight of steps to the Great Hall; the entrance now is through the 19th-century porch at ground level. Through this we enter the Undercroft, now resplendent with 16th- and early 17th-century Byron tombs which have been brought here from the ruined church at Colwick. And so into the *Cloisters*: on the E side is the former Chapter House (beautiful EE work), which since the 16th century has been used as the chapel. It was redecorated *c.*1860 by Mr Webb and glows with Victorian colouring and glass. On the W side a staircase leads up into the *Gallery* above the cloister: here there are many exhibits and pictures connected with Byron, and in the N Gallery, above an 18th-century marble chimneypiece, there is a portrait of Boatswain, Byron's beloved dog; from the windows all around it is possible to look down into the cloister garth, with the 16th-century cistern as its centrepiece. A newel staircase leads up to the *Prior's Chamber*, which was Byron's bedroom, where we can admire the bed made for him for his rooms at Cambridge, gloriously adorned with coronets. On the W side of the Gallery a door leads into the Great Hall, redecorated by John Shaw in the most splendid Tudor style; on the S side is the Saloon, converted from the Refectory, with an early 17th-century plaster and panelled ceiling. There are smaller rooms on the E side: the most interesting is the *Charles II Room*, with Palladian decoration à la William Kent. Only a lawn now occupies the nave and choir of the church, but close to the spot where the high altar stood stands the tomb of Boatswain. On a stand of circular steps the elegant octagonal monument, surmounted by an urn, is inscribed 'Near this spot are deposited the remains of one who possessed Beauty without Vanity, Strength without Insolence, Courage without Ferocity, and all the Virtues of man without his Vices. This praise, which would be unmeaning Flattery if inscribed over human ashes, is but a just tribute to the memory of BOATSWAIN a dog, who was born at Newfoundland May 1803, and died at Newstead November 18 1808.' The poet's lines in praise of

his faithful friend follow, of which the last four may be quoted: 'Ye! who perchance behold this simple urn/Pass on – it honours none you wish to mourn;/To mark a friend's remains these stones arise: I never knew but one – and here he lies.' Byron wished to be buried here himself, next to Boatswain; he had to be content with Hucknall Church. The setting of Newstead is incomparable: to the E the square *Eagle Pond* is surrounded by terraces with lead figures on pedestals (perhaps by John Nost)—a formal garden laid out by the 4th Lord Byron. Romantic and exotic gardens laid out in the 19th century lie to the S, including Webb's *Japanese Garden*. Little remains, alas, of the buildings and follies created by the 5th ('wicked') Lord Byron, who built a mock castle on the hillside, and kept a man o' war on the lake to entertain his friends: only his Gothick fort by the lakeside survives. After his disgrace following the duel fought with Mr Chaworth in Pall Mall he deliberately ran everything down, and neglected the house to snub his heir, his great nephew 'the brat in Aberdeen'. Yet the brat came to adore Newstead, and deeply regretted having to part with it. It was he who made the name Byron immortal, and it is his spirit which pervades the place today.

Normanton-on-Soar [13] The village street runs parallel with the river: there are several good brick houses, a late 16th-century timbered cottage with thatched roof, and a medieval stone *dovecote*, with 17th-century brick gabled top, in the grounds of the Victorian manor house. The *Church* stands on the very bank of the Soar, with views across the river to Loughborough, and is venerable and magnificent with tall, central broach spire, long chancel, aisleless nave, and transepts: it is chiefly of the 13th century, but the nave clerestory and N transept are by W.S. Weatherly

(1896). The interior is scraped, but there are a few old pews and a rare Royal Arms of Charles II in plaster above the chancel arch (1683); and two small, early 17th-century Willoughby monuments, with kneeling figures, in the chancel.

Normanton-on-Trent [9] A quiet, withdrawn, secluded village on the back lane from Sutton to Marnham and the isolated countryside near the river—an undiscovered place. There are several good houses: the *Grange*, a late 17th-century brick building in the main street, and the Hall, an early 19th-century stuccoed house next to the church; and several pretty, smaller houses. Modest but attractive *Church* of varying dates: 14th-century nave with clerestory, with the Perp tower built into the W arches of the nave. Brass memorial, within stone frame, to Robert Curtys, Vicar of the parish (1680); one or two later monuments; and a window in the chancel by Mayer of Munich (1855).

Norwell [9] (pronounced Norrell) Norwell Overhall . . . Norwell Pallishall . . . Norwell Tertia Pars . . . There were three Prebendaries of Norwell in Southwell Minster until the early 19th century, each with a Prebendal house at Southwell, each with a manor here (Norwell, of course, is the North Well, just as Southwell is the South Well). Norwell with its *moated sites* is a romantic place. There is a complete moat, still filled with water, beside the church (Norwell Overhall); another (Pallishall) off the lane to Bathley still retains a fragment of its ancient house; a third (Tertia Pars) is behind the cottages N of the village street; besides these there is another at Norwell Woodhouse, and yet another (Willoughby-in-Norwell) at a remote and willowy spot off the lane to Carlton. Norwell is a village of old brick cottages and larger houses; the old school is early 18th century; there is even a fanciful Victorian Gothic one; the

Normanton-on-Soar

Grange, near the church, and in distant days the vicarage, is late 18th century, with two porches, a drawing room decorated in trompe l'œil by Thomas Errington, and a charming garden. The *Church* with its big sturdy tower with low pyramid roof and little pinnacles, has an air. It is a spacious building of the 14th and 15th centuries, with transepts, Geometrical E window, Perp clerestory; there are early monuments, including the effigy of a 14th-century lady and later ones (S transept) to tenants of the prebendal manors, of which the best has plenty of heraldry and an indecipherable inscription. The organ is perched high up over the tower arch, and looks as though it has been temporarily hoisted by pulleys. This is countryside of woodlands and wide views, some of the best in the county, unfrequented, little known. The *lane to Bathley* is a special delight.

North Clifton, *see* Clifton, North

North Collingham, *see* Collingham, North

North Leverton, *see* Leverton, North

North Muskham, *see* Muskham, North

North Wheatley, *see* Wheatley, North

Nottingham* [14] 'The Queen of the Midlands'. Nottingham has a long history; there was a Saxon settlement here, then a Danish borough. Soon after the Conquest William Peverel built the original Norman castle, and during the Middle Ages the town grew and prospered on wool and cloth. It was here that Charles I raised his standard on 22 August 1642: it was here that the Civil War began. Eighteenth-century pictures show a handsome town, with big Georgian houses standing in spacious grounds; later in the century and during the Victorian era the place grew enormously as industry took over. But much remains. Nottingham is enormous, but venerable and individual among the great cities of England. Even today the great castle stands on one hill, the great church of St Mary on the other; round St Mary's the narrow streets with the old warehouses give the *Old Town* an air—not unlike the old narrow streets of the City of London; many fine Georgian houses line the long street—High Pavement, Middle Pavement, Low Pavement—between St Mary's and the Castle, and there are still the three old parish churches in the middle of the town. There are, of course, the vast factories—Boots, Player's, Raleigh Bicycles—and the suburbs seem to go on for ever. But there are wonderful parks and open spaces, the University occupies one of the most splendid sites of any modern seat of learning, and great tree-lined boulevards sweep around the western side of the town. The *Market Place* is one of the largest in England.

This is the ideal starting point for a tour of the town. The square—affectionately known as 'Slab Square'—is dominated by the great domed *Council House* (by the Nottingham architect Cecil Howitt, 1927), a magnificent 1920s baroque palace which is now beginning to come into its own once more; its booming chimes reverberate round the near-by streets. Most of the buildings are Victorian; one Georgian survivor is *Bromley House* (1752) in Angel Row, the town house of Sir George Smith, the banker, grandson of Thomas Smith, founder of Smith's Bank, progenitor of the National Provincial (now, of course, part of National Westminster), ancestor of Smiths, Abel Smiths, Vivian Smiths, Dorrien Smiths, Bromleys, and Lord Carrington; it now houses that admirable institution, the Nottingham Subscription Library. Though the front door is now wedged in between shops, the splendid staircase ascends to the first floor rooms, with their distinguished plasterwork and fittings. Near by, the *Bell Inn* is an old house, and *Yates's Wine Lodge*, opposite, is attractive with its iron colonnade outside, its cast-iron galleries within. On the same side, on the corner of King Street, is Watson Fothergill's *Queen's Chambers* (1897), and between King Street and Queen Street on its prominent triangular site looking down into the square stands Waterhouse's *Prudential Insurance Building*—unmistakably Waterhouse; opposite is the Italianate head office of *Smith's Bank* (1878); near by the *Flying Horse*, an old, much restored, timber-framed house with overhanging gables. Leaving the Market Place by Bridlesmith Gate and walking S, we enter Middle Pavement, and turning left and carrying on, we reach High Pavement, with the former *High Pavement Unitarian Chapel* on the corner. Built in 1876 by Stuart Colman, the interior is an important gallery of Burne-Jones and Morris glass: it is no longer used as a church, and is now (1983) being converted into a museum; just beyond is the *County Hall* with its grand Ionic portico (by James Gandon, 1769); opposite, the *Judges' Lodging*, an 18th-century house with an imposing addition by Moses Wood (1833) to house the judges' dining room. And so we reach *St Mary's*, one of the great town churches of England. Cruci-form, with dominating central tower, long nave, long chancel, wide, spacious transepts, the church was almost entirely built in the early 15th century. Note especially the bronze S door by Henry Wilson (1904), the enormous windows of the transepts, the stone panelling of the interior walls, the glass by Morris; Kempe; Hardman; Heaton, Butler and Bayne; Ward and Hughes; Burlison and Grylls; Clayton and Bell (nearly all the great Victorian designers), and the wealth of 18th-century monuments which line the walls. There is one to John Holles, Duke of Newcastle; one to Thomas Smith the banker; and a specially touching one to Henry Plumptre—b.1708, d.1718/19—'In these few and tender years he had to a great degree made himself Master of the Jewish, Roman and English History, the Heathen Mythology and the French tongue, and was not inconsiderably advanced in the Latin', so the inscription tells us.

From St Mary's it is possible to explore the narrow streets of the Lace Market, and the great warehouses (several by T.C. Hine)—*Broadgate* is specially rewarding—and then we may retrace our steps down *High Pavement*, noting in particular a number of Georgian houses (e.g. Willoughby House, No 18 next door, and the Post Office opposite, with its impressive façade of Corinthian columns). At Lister Gate turn right to *St Peter's*, another notable church, chiefly of the 13th and 14th centuries, with tall pinnacled spire; beautifully furnished interior with Schnetzler organ case (1770), another fine display of Victorian glass, and many monuments; Low Pavement turns into Castlegate, but is dissected by the terrible new road called Maid Marian Way (even the name is objectionable), which has been hailed as 'one of the ugliest roads in Europe'. Here *St Nicholas's* stands, almost buffeted by the swirling traffic of this inner relief road—an interesting church of 1671, built to replace a predecessor destroyed in

---

* Named districts of Nottingham are to be found in alphabetical order immediately following this entry on central Nottingham (p. 126).

119

Nottingham; The Market Place

Boots' original shop

the Civil War; the church was enlarged in the 18th century, and the interior has been spoiled, but there are some 17th- and 18th-century furnishings, and an 18th-century plaster ceiling to the chancel. Castlegate continues beyond the dual carriageway: there are more notable 18th-century houses, such as No 19, in the Adam style; No 64 is specially interesting (in fact late 17th century) as the house where Marshal Tallard came to live in 1705 after the defeat of Blenheim; he was well treated, and indeed cultivated by the local aristocracy, and here he laid out a French garden. Farther up there are smaller houses (one is a Costume Museum), and the *Castle* is upon us.

Little remains of the medieval castle, apart from a few foundations, and the (much restored)

14th-century gatehouse. The site was purchased after the Civil War by William Cavendish, 1st Duke of Newcastle (of Welbeck and Bolsover), who began to build the new castle in 1674. He was probably his own architect, assisted by Samuel Marsh; the new building contributes little to the skyline (unlike Bolsover), but as a grand Italian palazzo it is, of course, superb—still superb, despite the disaster of 1831. The E front surveyed the town, the S and W sides the park below and the countryside beyond. The building is rusticated; Ionic columns support the entablature; pedimented, balconied windows serve the *piano nobile*, smaller windows the ground and top floors. The emphasis is severe, horizontal; it is a palace, not a castle. It passed to the Pelham and Pelham-Clinton Dukes of Newcastle: in 1831 the mob, in-

flamed by the 'reactionary' 4th Duke of Newcastle's opposition to the Reform Bill, set fire to the castle; all the interiors were burnt out, and it remained a roofless shell until 1876, when it was purchased by the town and T.C. Hine converted the interior into a *Museum*. It is well worth a visit: there is a collection of medieval Nottingham alabaster carvings, a notable collection of silver, and a picture gallery, with many pictures by Richard Parkes Bonington (a native of Arnold), and much else. There are, of course, great views from the terrace.

Beneath the Castle to the S is *Brewhouse Yard* (little 17th-century houses, now a museum) and the celebrated inn, *The Trip to Jerusalem* (also 17th century, but dating back to the time of the Crusades, and extending into the caves in the Castle Rock); to the S is the *Park*. In the

St Mary's, **Nottingham**

early 19th century the 4th Duke of Newcastle decided to develop the ancient deer park for residential purposes: at the top of the hill, *Park Terrace* (1827) is like a stuccoed Regency terrace in Brighton—but on the W side the houses overlook not the sea, but gardens descending the steep hillside below, and the later houses of the Park. Even here, however, there is an inkling of seaside architecture: there are wonderful Victorian houses of all shapes and sizes, gay or gloomy as the architects or their patrons might decide, in brick or stucco, Gothic or Classical, or merely inimitable T.C. Hine or Watson

opposite and above **Nottingham**: The Lace Market

Fothergill. The Park will repay a leisurely perambulation.

Retracing our steps, we can visit *Standard Hill* (commemorating 22 August 1642), and passing the Hospital and St James's Street (some noteworthy 18th century houses here too) to make for Regent Street, where No 25 was Hine's own house. So, through Wellington Circus, to the *Playhouse*. This remarkable new theatre, built between 1959 and 1964 (Peter Moro and Partners, architects) ranks with the Chichester Theatre as the most important theatre to be built since the war. As at Chichester, a few individuals were behind its founding: here Alan Rook, the poet, playwright and viticulturist, and a few friends were the founders. The exterior with its clean functional lines, looks sparkling when illumin-ated at night. It is one of the few modern buildings, that will pass the test of time.

Near by stands the RC Cathedral of St Barnabas, built in 1841 for the 8th Earl of Shrewsbury by Pugin. It is simple, austere, in Pugin's EE style, with central spire, entirely different from Pugin's great church at Cheadle (Staffs) for the same patron. Unfortunately much of Pugin's interior decoration has been swept away—it is all sterilized, according to modern fashion—and with it so much of the numinous has gone; a stark, central, holy table stands at the crossing; the tyranny of 'fashion': poor Pugin, poor Nottingham.

From here we can walk across to Upper Parliament Street; on the left, looking down Market Street into the Market Place, is the *Theatre Royal*, with its stuccoed façade and portico reminiscent of the Haymarket; and so on to Lower Parliament Street. Here we can turn right into George Street, where stands an incredible building, *Watson Fothergill's own office*, a *tour de force* of High Victorian art, with busts of Pugin and Street, and the names of Scott and Burges and Norman Shaw inscribed in the decoration, adorning a façade already resplendent with stone, terracotta, and timber. Near by, in Thurland Street, is his purer Gothic, *National Westminster Bank*—a very successful building.

To the N of Upper Parliament Street stand, in or around Trinity Square, *the Guildhall* (1887) and the original *University College* (1877), and other buildings now part of the Trent Polytechnic. Near by is the

In Castlegate

Middle Pavement

site of Victoria Station, the glory of the old Great Central Railway. Only the clock tower and the Victoria Hotel survive of what was a station as fine as a London terminus. In its place there is yet another shopping 'centre' and a string of gargantuan blocks of flats: an eyesore. Up Mansfield Road stands St Andrew's Church with its conspicuous stocky spire, a large, prosperous Victorian building (by William Knight, 1869); a little farther on is the Forest Recreation Ground where the Goose Fair is now held every October. The *Arboretum* (down Waverley Street) is a smaller Victorian public park of evocative charm. Nottingham High School (Arboretum Street) is in a suitable collegiate Gothic style (1866–7 by Simpson and Hine). On the other side of Waverley Street stands All Saints', in Hine's rather heavy Gothic (1863), a large church with broach spire, and matching vicarage and church hall.

The Midland Station is in Carrington Street, S of the Market Place, unmistakably Midland Railway, and built in red brick and terracotta, with a low, domed clock tower: as a building Victoria far outshone it. London Road leads down to Trent Bridge (*see* West Bridgford) past the district called the Meadows; *St George's*, here, is worth a visit (Kirkwhite Street), a spacious, bellcoted church (by R.C. Sutton, 1877), with impressive sanctuary, Lady chapel and other chapels by Bodley (1897), a building with a powerful religious atmosphere. Along the N bank of the Trent runs the *Victoria Embankment*, a delightful riverside drive laid out in 1920. There is a great triumphal arch as a war memorial (First World War), and a noble statue of Queen Victoria. The suspension (foot) bridge leads across to West Bridgford. This is about the extent that even the most energetic walker will wish to explore on foot: for the suburbs a car will be necessary, and these may be best classified alphabetically.

top The Castle ▷
bottom The Park

Named districts of Nottingham

Arnold The relics of the old village lie to the E of the Mansfield Road: there is one tall 18th-century house, the birthplace of Bonington the painter. The *old Church* is up the hill and dates from the early 14th century; in the chancel is a somewhat mutilated Easter sepulchre. *St Paul's, Daybrook*, on the main road, built by Pearson for the Seely family (1892), with its tall spire, reminiscent of Truro

and Kilburn, and inspired by Coutances, is in Pearson's later Geometrical style (e.g. All Saints', Hove, 1890); all of stone, and very fine. Near by is the vast Home Brewery, and there are other imposing 1930s factories on the main road recalling contemporary developments on the Great West Road. Nearer Nottingham is the *RC Church of the Good Shepherd, Woodthorpe*, by Gerald Goalen (1963), with its concrete vaulting and graceful concrete pillars, and a glorious display of glass by Patrick Reyntiens: a moving and numinous church.

Basford A few old houses of the old village, and a 13th-century church with an ornate tower of 1859 (by Thomas Allom), close to the River Leen and uncomfortably hemmed in by railway lines and main roads. Spacious, well-furnished interior with elegant 13th-century arcades; unusual Victorian reredos and E window in memory of Ichabod Wright the banker, of Mapperley Hall. Factories and Victorian housing climb the hill to New Basford: in High Church Street, appropriately, is *St Augustine's* (by G.G. Place, 1859 and later), with its devout interior. Farther out to the NW (Nuthall Road) is Christ Church, Cinderhill (by T.C. Hine, 1856)—again appropriately named: it is close to Babbington colliery.

Beeston An old village, overtaken in the 19th century by textile mills and Victorian housing, and now submerged in modern suburbia. The *parish Church* was rebuilt in 1842 (by Scott and Moffatt), but the 15th-century chancel survives. A spacious interior: two Royal Arms (George III and Victoria), a few monuments, and hatchment of the Rickards family. Near by the *Manor House* is 17th-century brick, with 18th-century Gothick windows, and there are other unexpected and attractive old houses in pretty gardens. There are several 19th-century mills, of which the *Anglo Scotian* of 1871 is a dramatic Gothic building with four floors of big lancet windows, battlements and turrets. And Sir Owen Williams's *Boot's Factory*, built in 1930, is justly celebrated and often illustrated—one of the first buildings of glass and concrete, functional and pleasing.

Bestwood Across a sea of suburban houses, not far from the industry of Daybrook, the pyramid-crowned tower, the gabled silhouette, the many chimneys of Teulon's masterpiece appear on the skyline (off Mansfield Road turn W into

The Anglo Scotian Mill, **Beeston**

Oxclose Lane, then N into Bestwood Lodge Drive). Suddenly suburbia ends, a notice proclaims 'Bestwood Lodge Hotel', and the road becomes a park drive. The house crowns its low hill, the drive turns the final corner, passes a grand stable block and delivers us into the entrance courtyard. *Bestwood Lodge* was built in 1862–5 by S.S. Teulon for the 10th Duke of St Albans, descendant of Charles II and Nell Gwynn. The King had granted to his son Charles Beauclerk the old royal hunting lodge of Bestwood: it was here that his descendant decided to build a new house of some grandeur. The entrance courtyard is not large. It is dominated by a

Bestwood Lodge

tall, narrow entrance tower with a high pyramid roof: gables and chimneys, bay windows and flying buttresses, a lower staircase turret, a black-and-white wing on the right (a later alteration), a servants' hall on the left, designed to look like a chapel—the whole composition is spiky, asymmetrical, and built in flaming red brick; Teulon's buildings are always original, and always aggressive. Inside, the two-storeyed, galleried hall is the grandest room; the former drawing room and dining room (now one large restaurant) are fair-sized rooms—but not specially grand or ducal. Inside and out there are flourishes and flashes of inspiration—a French dormer here, a crocketed pinnacle there, arcades of moulded red brick, columns of polished marble, carved panels by Thomas Earp—yet there is something restless, something incomplete about the house: it has a contrary, awkward, High Victorian character which is at once irritating and endearing. It is a pleasure that the house is now an hotel, and readily accessible; the position is attractive, and there are views from the main rooms to gardens and woodlands, with no hint of the sprawling suburbs at its gates. Below the Lodge, and easily missed, is the little *Church*, also built by Teulon for the family (1868). This is of stone and bellcoted, with an apsidal E end adorned with stained glass by Morris, and murals, recently restored by Imogen Skirving and David Rowbotham. There are family memorials: the 10th and 11th dukes are buried here, and round the corner at the W end is a monument with bust to Sir John Huddleston 'last created Baron of the Exchequer and Member of the Order of the Coif' (1898), who married the sister of the 10th duke. One more great Victorian monument at Bestwood is the *Pumping Station*, close to the A60 (Mansfield Road), where it rears its immensely tall tower above the trees and shrubberies that surround it. Built in

West Bridgford

1871 in a kind of Florentine Gothic, it stands here brooding—stupendously unexpected and, externally, the finest of Nottinghamshire's Victorian pumping stations.

Bilborough A great sea of suburban housing: only a few cottages of the old village survive, the Regency *Old Rectory*, and the little 14th-century *church*. It contains a monument to Sir Edmund Helwys of Broxtowe Hall (demolished in 1937), who died in 1590, a forebear of the Elwes family. A rather formless addition to the church was made in 1972.

Bramcote The village street, between the Derby road (A52) and Chilwell, is narrow and passes through a deep canyon: old cottages, one or two larger houses, the tower of the medieval church—replaced in 1881 by the new *Church* with its blackened broach spire (by John Johnson), containing a 13th-century font, monument to Henry Hanley (1650), later monuments to the Sherwin Gregorys of Bramcote

Hills (and Harlaxton) and one Gregory hatchment. *Bramcote Grange* with its Venetian windows is late 18th century and now part of St John's Theological College (the main buildings are at the bottom of the hill); *Bramcote House* is late Victorian, and on a magnificent site with dramatic views. The *Manor House* is of special interest, a rare 17th-century L-shaped brick house, built by the Hanley family on rising ground, and remarkably unaltered: a flight of steps leads up to the terrace, which is adorned with an early 18th-century wrought-iron balustrade; gables, mullioned windows and, inside, a panelled drawing room.

Bridgford, West Trent Bridge: holy ground for cricket lovers. The famous cricket ground was opened in 1838: the first county match (between Notts and Sussex) was played here soon after, and Test Matches soon after that. *Trent Bridge* itself was rebuilt in 1871 (there has been a bridge here since the Middle Ages), and the spans are adorned

Trent Bridge, **West Bridgford**

with ornamental cast iron by Handyside of Derby. The vast County Offices (by Vincent Harris, 1937) are 1930s Georgian, with a bright green copper roof: there is much to be said for them. The long residential roads lead off in all directions: substantial Victorian houses, large Edwardian villas, snug inter-wars semis. West Bridgford has almost the air of a seaside town. The 14th-century *parish Church* is now the S aisle of a spacious and sympathetic new church, added in 1896 by Naylor and Sale: well-furnished, prosperous interior, with 14th-century screen. The *Old Bowls Pavilion* is the home of the Nottinghamshire Building Preservation Trust; and *The Test Match* inn has a pleasant 1930s Georgian façade, and an Art Deco interior adorned with delightful topical murals by Leonard Huskinson.

Bulwell Completely submerged. A small market place, a Victorian *church* (by Stevens of Derby, 1850), an ancient dovecote and a charming little *school* of 1669, which has miraculously survived (now a private house): red brick, tiny Dutch gables, and porch with the arms of the Strelley family, painted and gilded.

Carlton Contiguous with Gedling: a 1930s cinema, Victorian villas and larger houses, shops, hosiery factories, and a (former) brewery by Watson Fothergill. The *Parish Church* is a grand red-brick Romanesque basilica (by W.A. Coombs), built for the 4th Earl of Carnarvon who had inherited all the Stanhope property through his wife: an unusual building with late Victorian furnishings (e.g. the hanging iron cross at the chancel steps). Nearer Nottingham a large former school building is inscribed 'Hindu Temple Nottingham'.

Carrington Between Sherwood Rise and Mapperley Plains—older, early 19th-century suburbia: a small Victorian streets and housing to the W, grander housing (especially in Mapperley Park) to the E. The

oldest church is St John's in Mansfield Road, built in 1843 in Commissioners' style, by the suitably named William Surplice, of Nottingham.

Chilwell Contiguous with Beeston: a small village overtaken by the textile industry in the 19th century. Homely roads were built among the old orchards: small Victorian (and later) houses in their gardens. A pleasant late Victorian church (1901), a few old houses and cottages—and the 1861—Tudor building of the former Baptist College.

Clifton was undoubtedly one of the prettiest of Nottinghamshire villages, with its broad green, long winding street, great cruciform church, its great house at the end overlooking the Trent, and the ancient trees of Clifton Grove lining the river bank. It was the home of one of Nottinghamshire's oldest families, who took their name from the place, and had given devoted service to the county over the centuries. Now all is changed: swirling traffic pours along the new link road to the M1, vast housing estates engulf the place on all sides, and the Cliftons have departed into voluntary exile in Hampshire. The village survives in its fossilized state: on *the Green* there is the 17th-century almshouse with its little gazebos, the white-stuccoed Old Rectory, and a tall brick dovecote; pretty cottages accompany the lane to the Church and the Hall. The *Church* has a tall central tower and includes work from the 12th century to the 15th; the 14th-century gable cross at the W end bears a carved Rood—a rare survival. The display of monuments inside is the finest in the county: there is a Sir Gervase, with the lion rampant of the Cliftons on his surcoat (late 14th century); a brass to Sir Robert (1478); a brass to another Sir Gervase (1491); and a great alabaster tomb to yet another Sir Gervase (1587) with his two wives. His son George

Clifton

died the same year, aged 20, five months before his father, and is commemorated by another brass, with his wife, Winifred Thorold, leaving a son who was but four months old at his grandfather's death. This child Gervase became the most celebrated of all the eleven Sir Gervase Cliftons: moreover he married seven times, and there is a grand architectural monument to his first three; it bears no effigies, but their arms on a black sarcophagus, and a gruesome collection of skulls and bones beneath. In the floor near by is the touching inscription which Sir Gervase composed for his grandmother who had brought him up: 'This stone covereth the body of Dame Anne Thorold, daughter of Sir John Constable of Kinolton Knt, and widdow of Sir Anthony Thorold of Marston in the county of Lincolne Knt, the most loveing and carefull grandmother of Sir Gervase Clifton Knt and Baronet, who laid the same for her, being a lady for her piety and exemplar virtues worthy to be had in perpetuall remembrance, and died heer August 1611.' Sir Gervase himself is commemorated by a monument with bust in the chancel (1666). There are many later monuments, and in the S transept a ledger stone to Joseph the Black Prince, a negro servant of the family, who died in 1685. Clifton Hall is now part of the *Trent Polytechnic*: the family resided here till 1953. John Carr remodelled the house *c*.1780: it now appears as a restrained red-brick Georgian house, with a Doric colonnade on the ground floor: to the discerning eye, however, there will appear vestiges of earlier gables and mullions. Inside, there is a grand octagonal hall (by Carr), lit by a top dome resplendent with delicate plasterwork. The Great Chamber has 17th-century panelling and a chimneypiece by John Smythson; the next room is called the Pages' Room, and is decorated with 17th-century paintings incorporated in the panelling. There are many good 18th-century rooms, and magnificent views from the house and the terrace down to the river.

Lenton font detail ▷

Colwick The river and the racecourse: from the 15th century to the 17th Colwick belonged to the Byrons and their early tombs, removed from the church here, are now at Newstead. The Musters family, London merchants, acquired Colwick in the 17th century, and built *the great house*. The entrance front (N) incorporates part of an early 18th-century house; the rest was rebuilt by Carr of York in 1776. The S front has a pedimented centrepiece with Ionic portico, and long one-storey wings containing great rooms. It is now an hotel, to serve the racecourse. The little church stands next door, roofless: it is partly Perp, partly of 1684. A new church has been built closer to human habitation. The Musters monuments are now at Annesley (q.v.).

Lenton A submerged village, close to inner Nottingham—submerged in the early 19th century. Little remains of the once great and powerful Lenton Priory: a small church, partly medieval, partly Victorian, is called the *Priory Church*, and was probably a chapel of the Priory Hospital; near by stands the base of a solitary pillar of the great church. There is a rare Royal Arms of Charles I in the small church. The large church of 1842 (by Stevens of Derby) contains the remarkable *12th-century font* from the Priory. It is rectangular, and its sides are carved with representations of Our Lord's Baptism, Crucifixion and Resurrection. It is one of the most notable fonts in England. The E window in memory of Francis Wright the founder (of the banking family) is extremely attractive with its floral designs (1873). Some pretty, Victorian buildings near the church (the School, and Church Grove); several charming houses down the old *village street* (Old Manor House, Vine Cottage and the *White Hart*).

No modern university in England can equal Nottingham in its situation and spacious buildings; this is due to the munificence of one man—Jesse Boot, first Lord Trent, founder of Boots Pure Drug Company. He bought the park at Lenton (W of the Clifton Boulevard) in 1920, and *University College*, originally founded in the heart of the city (see p. 123), moved out here in 1928 to the imposing building, designed by Morley Horder, overlooking the lake and landscaped park below. Built of glistening Portland stone, the *Trent Building* is a grand palace in 20th-century classical idiom: tree-shaded drives, spacious lawns are the setting for the halls of residence in the park behind, mostly built in a free neo-Georgian style, by a number of architects since the war; the original *Lenton Hall* is a castellated early 19th-century house, now the Hugh Stewart Hall. Cecil Howitt designed the *Portland Building*; Sir Percy Thomas was the supervising architect after university status was achieved in 1948.

Radford Older, inner, industrial Nottingham: the great *Player's Tobacco factory*, and the *Raleigh cycle works*. Old streets of artisan housing. *St Peter's*, in Hartley Road, is an aisleless Gothic barn of 1812 (by Moses Wood), with a later chancel of 1871.

Sneinton (pronounced Snenton) Nineteenth-century housing. The old *windmill*, recently restored, alone survives of the old village. But *St Stephen's* is a notable church, originally built by Rickman with a blackened central tower, and otherwise entirely rebuilt by C.G. Hare in 1912. It is a spacious cruciform building in Bodleian Perp, with splendid furnishings and wide vistas: reredos, font cover, organ in S gallery, and 15th-century chancel stalls from St Mary's; one of the best churches in Nottingham. *St Alban's* is by Bodley himself (1886), smaller, but lofty and impressive. It is now

used by the Orthodox Church. General Booth, founder of the Salvation Army, was born in *Notinton Place* (a little backwater of Georgian houses) in 1829. His statue in bronze stands outside the house, which is now a museum.

Wilford The church, and the early 18th-century rectory next door, on the S side of the river, are dwarfed by the enormous power station on the opposite bank. The *Church* is 14th and 15th century (N aisle added by Naylor and Sale in 1890): uniform embattled exterior and W tower. The poet Henry Kirk White was born here, and is buried in the churchyard. There are some older houses in the village street: the Hall is a big, square, brick house of 1791 (by William Henderson of Loughborough), built for a member of the Smith family, bankers.

Wollaton Though surrounded by Nottingham on all sides, the village is remarkably intact—with its small square, school, cottages, the *Admiral Rodney*, and the church. And the park, of course, is still enormous. Most of the *Church*, with its battlemented tower and recessed spire, is 14th century. Inside, there is an exceedingly handsome late 17th-century reredos, with Corinthian columns, broken pediment, and carved panels adorning the compartments. Unfortunately, the church has been 'reordered'—the altar moved to the centre, and the whole chancel now cluttered with seats; moreover the reredos has been painted white, so that it now looks like plasterwork: previously dark, with baroque ornaments on the altar, it looked magnificent, like the altar in some Wren church in London. The Willoughby tombs carry on the sequence at Willoughby-on-the-Wolds: brasses to Sir Richard and his wife (1471) under an elaborate canopy; the effigy of Sir Henry (1528), surrounded by the little figures of his four wives; and the later monuments to the 4th Lord Middleton (1800) by Bacon,

Wollaton

and the 6th Lord (1835) by West-macott. There is also the much more modest tablet to Robert Smythson (1614), 'Architect and Surveyor unto the most worthy house of Wollaton and divers others of great account'. This 'most worthy *house of Wollaton*' stands on its hill in the *Park*, supremely stately, self confident, unusual—even among the fantastic mansions reared in Elizabethan England. It was built between 1580 and 1588 by Sir Francis Willoughby, a man of ancient lineage with great aristocratic connections, yet himself a wealthy coal magnate and in-dustrialist: he paid for the stone from Ancaster with loads of coal from his own mines. The house is rectangular, with four corner towers rising above it, crowned with ornate gables, statues and obelisks; it is everywhere symmetri-cal, with large windows, classical pilasters, strapwork decoration, niches, busts, vases, chimneys adorning every surface and skyline. And, above all this, rising from the centre is the prodigious belvedere tower, with two tiers of traceried windows, and round turrets at the corners capped with lead domes, oddly at variance in form and design from the rest of the house. It is romantic, exciting—yet at the same time curious, clumsy and overbearing. No doubt Robert Smythson was here consciously aping the medieval (as his son John did at Bolsover). The lower windows of the belvedere light the Great Hall, those above an enor-mous empty 'Prospect Room', built solely for the view. The house has been much altered inside (by Wyatville in the early 19th century) and is now used as a *Natural History Museum*, so that little idea can be gained of the building as a house; only the Great Hall, occupying the centre of the building, and lit by its clerestory in the belvedere tower, retains any sense of Smythson's interior. Sir Francis Willoughby had no son: his elder daughter mar-ried a namesake, Sir Percival Wil-loughby, of the Willoughby de Eresby family, who were in no way related, and took their name from an entirely different Wil-loughby, in Lincolnshire. So their descendants represent a union be-tween the two great Willoughby families. In the 18th century Sir Thomas Willoughby, 2nd Bart, was created Lord Middleton, taking the title from another family property in Warwickshire; his son married

the heiress of Birdsall in Yorkshire, and as time went on Birdsall became the principal family home—as it is today. The 10th Lord Middleton sold Wollaton to the City of Nottingham in 1924. The place is excellently maintained: the house remains a monument to the curious genius of its builder and its architect.

Nuthall [10] Nuthall Temple, one of only four Palladian villas in England built in imitation of the Villa Rotonda at Vicenza, was pulled down in 1929; Foot's Cray Place was burnt down in 1950: only Chiswick House and Mereworth Castle survive. The loss of Nuthall is therefore a great tragedy. Even now, 50 years after this barbarism was committed, there remain the unmistakable traces of a great 18th-century layout. There is a long lime avenue running alongside the road towards Nottingham, there is the great sweep of a *landscaped park*, there are a few surviving great trees, a solitary cedar (always a sign of civilization) close to the site of the great house, and a solitary Palladian gatepier standing incongruously near some petrol pumps. Nuthall Temple was built in 1754 for Sir Charles Sedley by Stephen Wright of Durham (*see the Shell Guide to Co. Durham*), and adorned inside with sumptuous plasterwork by Roberts of Oxford; it passed by marriage to the Vernons of Sudbury, and was subsequently purchased, in 1819, by Robert Holden of Hawton (q.v.). Now the M1 roars past the site of this precious house: the 20th century cheerfully forgets the treasures of which it was not worthy. The *Church* is one of only five medieval churches in England dedicated to St Patrick: it is largely 14th century, though the base of the tower is 13th and the top 18th, which gives it a slightly odd character: there are a few small monuments to the Holdens, a 14th-century effigy to Sir Robert Cokefield, and a 15th-century screen. But the great thing is the medieval

glass: the E window contains the Crucifixion, and much heraldic glass, the S chancel window more heraldry, and many fragments. Close to the church stands the former rectory, with its compact but distinguished façade of pediment and Venetian windows, built in 1761. Little else remains of the old village: suburbia has taken over.

Oldcotes [5] Northernmost Nottinghamshire, at its most Yorkshire: a small village of stone cottages and a few larger houses, with a brook running through; there is one amazing spiky Victorian farmhouse, with great Gothicky farm buildings. Small C of E *Chapel of Ease* at the crossroads; unexpected and impressive *RC church* deeper in the village, with priest's house attached, and beautiful interior, built in 1869 by S.J. Nicholl for Mr Challenor of Hermeston Hall, standing on the site of a Roman villa. *Hermeston*, a plain stone house with restrained Gothic detail, was built by Mr Challenor *c.* 1848, and stands in its small park, shrouded by trees: it is now the home of his descendants, the Riddell family, a branch of the ancient Northumbrian Catholic family.

Ollerton [8] The old village is an oasis: a narrow street leads off the main road (A616), passes the Hall, and other old brick houses, and widens out into a broad central place watered by the little River Maun, dominated by the *Hop Pole Hotel*, a distinguished, pedimented 18th-century brick house, three storeys high, with lower wings; an old water mill astride the stream closes the vista, and a path leads up to the *Church* standing above the little street. Outwardly a plain stone building of 1780, with pinnacled tower and the plainest of Gothic windows, it is usually dismissed as of no interest: in fact the interior is charming, with its Gothick plaster panels painted soft apricot and white. A stone tablet from the earlier church commemorates

Thomas Markham, Lt-Col of Horse in the Royalist Army who was killed in a skirmish with the Roundheads in 1643; a brass plate in the sanctuary reads: 'The East Window is painted by C.G.S. Foljambe, Esqre of Cockglode in this parish, who at the same time caused the walls of the chancel to be lined with pine and the floor to be laid with tiles.' This is one of several windows erected in Notts churches by Mr Foljambe in memory of his wife (1873). Cockglode is no more—its site occupied by the Thoresby colliery. *Ollerton Hall* is an exceedingly fine, late 17th-century brick house standing close to the village street, its grounds sloping to the Maun. Two shallow wings embrace the entrance front, enlivened by plain stone pilasters: there are rows of long sash windows, a bold cornice, a hipped roof, a pedimented front door—but at present it is empty and unloved (1982); however, a rescuer is at hand. The house was built by the Markhams, a Papist branch of the great family, and descended from a younger son of Sir John Markham of Cotham (q.v.), and there was a secret Catholic chapel in the roof; they married into all the great recusant families—Arundells of Wardour, Salvins of Croxdale—while many daughters became nuns at Bruges or Pontoise. The eventual heiress married Marmaduke Tunstall of Wycliffe and died in 1791; so the Catholic history of Ollerton drew to its close. Ollerton is often called the Gateway to the Dukeries: indeed the splendid wooded parks of Thoresby and Rufford are close at hand. But with the coming of the coal-mines much has changed: the sweet air of Sherwood is laden with the sulphurous smell of coal, and the dukes are all dead or departed. But the name lives on, if only in the establishment in Wellow Road called the Dukeries Funeral Service. Incidentally, also in Wellow Road, the little Gothic house called *The Limes* should not be missed. The colliery village of New Ollerton adjoins to the N. The chimneys and winding towers raise their menacing heads above the newly landscaped grassy slagheaps: a large notice at the gate announces 'Vacancies', as though this were a boarding house. A neo-Queen-Anne police station, a neo-baroque public house called *The Plough*, an attractive and indeed impressive brick *Church* of 1931 (Naylor and Sale, architects), set on a grassy circle in a gloomy crescent—that is all there is to see. Otherwise it is the usual rows of shops, the usual rows of glum miners' houses, unrelieved by any of the charm of some later mining villages such as Rainworth or New Clipstone.

Ompton [8] Lovable for its name, and for its pretty red-brick cottages set in ample gardens; one has no path, no drive—just a long, wide, mown lawn leading up to the front door; there is a little Methodist chapel of 1860, all Georgian in character. Along the road towards Wellow—casting an eye across the quiet valley to the S—there is a glimpse of what appear to be three great pyramids, suddenly transported from Egypt, standing in a field; or approaching Wellow along the meandering lane from Eakring, they suddenly appear close at hand, rising through the morning mist perhaps, like an apparition. What are these? They are the *Ompton Pumping Station*, of the Severn-Trent Water Authority, built in 1965–8 (architect, David Jenkin): an undoubted, unexpected, Nottinghamshire attraction.

Orston [15] The road from the W crosses the little River Smite, and a wooded lane leads into the village. *Orston Hall* is a good-looking 18th-century house of stone and stucco, with sash windows and tall gatepiers, and an orchard towards the river aglow with snowdrops in early spring. There are good brick cottages in the street, and the Methodist chapel (1848) has

Gothick windows. The *Church* has a squat 18th-century tower (despised by the Victorians), and a light, spacious medieval nave and chancel, with 13th-century arcades and unusual Dec traceried windows in the aisle; there are a 17th-century font 'given by Mrs Constantia Kerchevall in 1662', a Royal Arms of George III, and a drum from the Battle of Waterloo. Gentle Belvoir countryside with wide views.

Ossington [8] The *lane from Moorhouse to Ossington* is one of the prettiest in Notts—secret, wooded, unfrequented. Suddenly, through a clearing in the trees, there is a glimpse of an 18th-century church, standing by itself above a lake; but there is no means of access. The lane leads on to the village: some good brick cottages, Ossington House, a small Calvary by the roadside. Turn left, and down a deeper, darker lane there are great gatepiers; this is the way to the church, and to the site of the Hall (demolished in 1963). The early Georgian house was built by the Cartwrights (*see* Marnham), and added to and altered by Lindley of Doncaster for their successors the Denisons (who happily still survive). The Cartwrights were a gifted family, the Denisons equally so: their most distinguished member was the Speaker of the House of Commons (1857–72), later created Viscount Ossington; of his younger brothers, one was bishop of Salisbury, another Governor-General of Australia. The *Church* was built in 1782 by Carr of York: the tower is surmounted by a cupola, the interior one of great charm, with triple arches dividing the sanctuary from the nave; there is a tomb (with brass) to Reynald Peckham (1551, his wife was a Cartwright), another, with kneeling figures, to William Cartwright (1602); at the W end Nollekens's sophisticated figures of William Denison (1782) and his brother Robert (1785) stand in niches. The Denisons were wealthy merchants

of Leeds, and the carved panel under William's statue depicts a ship unloading bales of wool for the clothing trade. And there are many other monuments to both families. The great house stood near by: the family now live at *Ossington House* (the former rectory), an exceedingly attractive 18th-century house, tactfully and skilfully enlarged in 1959. Close to the park gates, embowered in shrubberies, is a canopied well, built of stone and terracotta in memory of Edward Denison, son of the bishop of Salisbury, who died in 1870, aged 30, erected by Lady Ossington. It was designed by John Birnie Philip.

Owthorpe [14] In the winding, wandering lanes of the Vale of Belvoir: a tiny hamlet, a farm or two, some cottages. The little *Church* with low square tower and high-pitched hipped roof looks rather like a camel sitting all on its own in the fields here, surrounded by old stone walls, a pair of dilapidated gatepiers on the S leading nowhere. It is a 17th-century patchwork of great charm; the N wall is medieval, and medieval fragments have been reused elsewhere—above the W door two angels display a little shield. Inside, box pews, a two-decker pulpit, a heavy-arched screen dividing nave from chancel, and Hutchinson monuments. Colonel John Hutchinson, the regicide, retired here after the Civil War and built a substantial house with shaped gables, laying out gardens, canals and avenues, and cutting vistas through the woods—one to catch a glimpse of Langar Hall, one towards Belvoir, 'which as the afternoon sun sets full upon it made a glorious object'. Hutchinson was no extremist, and after the Civil War his name was included in the Act of Oblivion; but in 1663 he was arrested and imprisoned in Sandown Castle, Kent, where he died in 1664. His monument on the N wall of the church was erected by his wife and biographer Lucy Hutchinson: 'He died at Sandowne

Castle in Kent, after 11 months harsh and strict imprisonment without crime or accusation, upon the 11th day of September 1663 [this is incorrect: he died in 1664] in the 49th year of his age ... Quousque Domine?' His descendants sold the property to the Bromleys of East Stoke towards the end of the 18th century, and after standing empty for 40 years the house was demolished. An engraving made at this time shows it with sash windows replacing the mullions, the garden overgrown. Traces of the colonel's canals and plantations may still be traced in the fields near the church.

Oxton [11] A delightful village: old brick cottages and larger houses, the church, the school, the plantations of the park—all against the backdrop of the well-wooded hillside. The great attraction of the *Church* is the wide, 18th-century S aisle, with its sub-Gothick windows, and the 18th-century box pews throughout the church; all this gives the building enormous character. There is, of course, a low Norman chancel arch, and the nave arcades are early 14th-century: they 'die out' into the tower, added later in the century; there are 17th-century altar rails, and much 17th-century panelling and woodwork in the chancel. The church has a great display of Sherbrooke hatchments, a very fine George II Royal Arms (an extra I added later, to serve for George III), monuments to the Sherbrookes, too: the one to Admiral Rupert St Vincent Sherbrooke, VC (1972) is accompanied by the White Ensign which he flew in HMS *Onslow* on the Russian convoys; there is another flown by his father Captain Henry Sherbrooke, DSO in HMS *Tarantula* in 1917. In the floor by the N door is a beautifully inscribed stone to Gilbert Darwin of Marsett House (d.1979): 'He served his fellow men'. Oxton Hall, which stood to the N of the church, was the home of the Sherbrookes, a large square

Nollekens figure, **Ossington**

Papplewick outside. . . .

it is a late Georgian Gothick jewel. The tower is 14th century, the rest of 1795, with crocketed pinnacles, battlements, quatrefoils everywhere, and 'F.M. 1795' inscribed in the ogee spandrel of the lofty porch. F.M. was the Hon Frederick Montagu, politician, patron of the muses, friend of William Mason and Thomas Gray; his tomb stands near the tower, like an 18th-century marble table on slender legs. As an antiquary and man of taste he placed in his new porch the 12th-century carving of St James from the old church, and two early slabs to Sherwood Forest officials, together with two more just inside the door—ornamented with bellows, bow and arrow or hunting horn. The interior is elegant: opposite the door a double staircase ascends, the right-hand flight to the gallery, the left-hand flight to—nothing! The gallery runs along the N side and round to the W; there are contemporary altar rails, a walnut pulpit, a little marble font like a flower bowl standing on a pedestal, the Royal Arms of George III, a few hat pegs in the squire's gallery, fragments of 15th-century glass, and an E window, by Eginton, of Faith and Hope, after Reynolds's window in New College Chapel. From the N side of the church there is a view of the *Hall*, standing on rising ground, tall and gracious. The house is almost square: Ionic pilasters support a pediment on this W side: there is a more severe composition for the entrance front on the E. Inside, a cantilevered staircase, with graceful wrought-iron balustrade, surrounds the hall. Drawing Room, Dining Room and Library are decorated in sophisticated Adam style, but the architect is unrecorded. Robert Adam is claimed: Carr of York or Lindley of Doncaster are more likely candidates. It is not a large house, but it is most accomplished. There is yet another masterpiece at Papplewick: the *Victorian Pumping Station*, in Longdale Lane. The exterior is imposing, but

Georgian house, demolished in 1957. The family now live at the tall, gabled 17th-century house to the S of the church. The stables of the Hall, stuccoed and surmounted by a cupola, still stand; the family first came to Oxton in the 16th century, taking their name from Shirebrook in Derbyshire. They have given distinguished service to the county and the nation: General Sir John Sherbrooke was second-in-command to Wellington in the Peninsular War (1809), and subsequently Governor-General of Canada; Robert Lowe, 1st and last Viscount Sherbrooke, was Chancellor of the Exchequer and Home Secretary (d.1892), an accomplished scholar and eloquent speaker.

Papplewick [11] The village is intact, for all the proximity of Nottingham and Hucknall, of collieries and industry. Stone cottages, one or two larger houses, the late 18th-century Hall in a small park, the *Church* at the end of a side lane, easily missed. It must not be missed:

.... and inside

the interior is breathtaking. The engines are, of course, magnificent, but it is the decoration of the building that is even more remarkable. Pillars support the roof or the galleries, adorned with delicate panels of reeds and long-stalked water flowers and grasses amid which beautiful fish are moving: the capitals are formed of cranes and water birds. Polished brass is everywhere; there is stained glass in the windows, a portrait of Queen Victoria. Although no longer in use, the pumping station is frequently open to the public, and 'in steam' on high days and holidays.

Plumtree [14] The village has become swollen with a new commuter population from Nottingham, but the centre is still attractive, and is dominated by its ancient *Church*. A handsome embattled exterior, an austere embattled tower—the antiquity of the building is at once apparent when the great Norman doorway on the W front of the tower is seen. The rest of the church is 13th and 14th century, and all was beautifully restored by Bodley and Garner in 1873. To them is due the rood screen, the furnishing of

the chancel (and the stencilling of the chancel roof), the seating in the nave, the tactful rebuilding of the N aisle, the organ, and the repaving of the church. Stained glass by Burlison and Grylls adds to the restrained but rich colouring of the interior. On the S side of the church stands the early 19th-century rectory (now private house): the Revd John Burnside (1816–65), and the Revd William (1865–83), held the living for most of the 19th century: it was William who employed Bodley on the church.

Radcliffe-on-Trent [14] The red cliffs of the River Trent: a short walk along the road to Shelford, and there they are. Radcliffe is an overgrown village, a kind of satellite to Nottingham: the village sprouted mid-Victorian terraces and later Victorian houses, and in the 20th century well-to-do 'residential properties'. It is not unattractive. The street (from Nottingham) twists and turns: the centre is well treed and has an air. Few buildings of interest: the *Manvers Arms* is the double of a Manvers estate farmhouse at Budby (q.v.), and the large and prosperous *Church* was built in 1879 by Goddard and Paget of Leicester. It has a tall tower with a saddleback roof; an impressive lofty interior; small brass to Anne Ballard (1626); many good slate headstones in the churchyard.

Radford, *see* Nottingham

Ragnall [9] Tiny sequestered village, straggling along a by-road parallel with the Trent in that isolated power station country which borders the river here. The small *Church* with low tower, much rebuilt by Ewan Christian (1867), contains a monument by William Stanton (1690) to William Mellish (*see* Blyth), gloriously carved with cherubs and swags, and a colourful E window by Wailes. Opposite the church is the smallest of small village shops with the smallest of small

village pubs under the same roof. The Hall is a 19th-century farmhouse, but in its outbuildings are fragments of the 17th-century mansion of the Mellish family. Nicholas Hawksmoor was born here in 1611—of a yeoman farming family who held land here and at East Drayton (which also claims him). 'He was born a scholar' ran his obituary notice 'and knew as well the learned as the modern tongues, and was a very learned mathematician, geographer and geometrician.' He was a protégé of William Mellish, and at the age of 18 became clerk to Sir Christopher Wren.

Rainworth [11] (pronounced Ran'rth or Ren'rth) At the junction of the Newark–Mansfield road (A617) and the back road from Southwell: a mining village with rows of attractive, cottagey miners' houses, and the Robin Hood Inn, a near double of the Plough at Ollerton. There is a brick *Church* by Cecil Howitt, completed just before the last war, all furnished in dark oak and Mowbray blue, attractive architecturally, warm and religious in atmosphere.

Rampton [6] The gargantuan cooling towers, the enormous single chimney, of Cottam power station brood over the flat fields that border the Trent and dominate the landscape to the E; away to the W the spreading buildings of the Mental Hospital form a city of their own, a garden city of the 1930s, with the hospital buildings and houses for the staff in tree-lined setting. The village lies between: a church with a narrow 14th-century tower, a Victorian arched gateway to the Manor, red-brick houses, and the *Eyre Arms*. The charm of the *Church* is its wide, white interior, with light streaming through the old clear glass of the 17th-century windows in the S aisle on to the 14th- and 15th-century nave arcades, a Norman font and, in the chancel, a great assembly of monuments to the

Eyres. The finest, with cherubs and garlands and signed William Holland of London (1703), is to George Eyre: 'In him were found all those virtues by the exercise of which his ancestors so eminently distinguished themselves, one of whom, Colonel Eyre, for the service of his country and Royal Master, Charles the Martyr, lost his life in the defence of Newark Castle'; another commemorates Anthony Eyre of Grove, MP, who married the heiress of Sir Hardolph Wasteneys, last baronet of Headon (q.v.); another—signed Crace, Portland Road, London—Anthony Hardolph Eyre, MP (1836); his daughter married Granville Harcourt-Vernon (*see* Grove). There are tablets to Vice-Admiral Sir George (1839), and Major-General Sir William: 'History will gratefully record his services for his country' (1859); and to many others. There is a hatchment of Eyre, with Wasteneys in pretence; and on the floor the incised slabs to earlier owners: the manor descended from the Maulovels to the Stanhopes and Babingtons, and so to the Eyres. At the NE corner of the churchyard stands the remarkable, stone *Tudor gateway*, attached to a long brick wall, which has survived from the ancient Hall, demolished in 1736 when the family migrated to Grove. A later generation, descended from a younger branch, built a neo-Elizabethan house (designed by William Burn) in 1851—approached by the Victorian gateway W of the church. The Eyres departed finally at the end of the century and the newer house, sadly decapitated and deprived of Burn's gables and flourishes, and now converted into flats, stands marooned up its long, somewhat overgrown drive. The end of a long chapter.

Ranby [5] The new dual carriageway of the A1 roars past; but this is really a canalside village, with the old cottages facing the calm waters of the Chesterfield Canal. Little red-brick *Church* (1950). *Ranby House* has an early 20th-century Tudor front, but the long wing at the back is 18th century. It is the prep school for Worksop College. *Ranby Hall*, deep in woodlands to the N, is an interesting 18th- and early 19th-century house. It was the dower house for Clumber. *Morton Hall* stands in a beautiful wooded park to the S and is the home of the Mason family. The big Victorian–Elizabethan house has been replaced by a smaller house. The *gardens* are celebrated.

Ranskill [5] The Old North Road: a bellcoted Victorian *Church* (by Ewan Christian, 1878) on the main road, and a number of good brick houses, cottages and farm buildings along the side road to Blyth.

Ratcliffe-on-Soar [13] The diminutive village looks well from the new road (A648) that links Nottingham and the M1—a church with a blackened stone spire, and a gabled manor farmhouse next door, set in the watery meadows of the River Soar. On the other side of the main road stands the enormous power station, with its double phalanx of gargantuan cooling towers; and the railway rattles by on the E. Hemmed in by road, railway, river and power station, the village miraculously survives. The broach spire of the *Church*, with its four little pinnacles, is EE, as is the chancel with its double lancet windows: the S aisle is a delightful patchwork of stone and brick with Dec windows, and there are Georgian windows in the N aisle; inside, spacious nave with 14th-century arcades, and even more spacious chancel. This is the setting for the spectacular tombs of the Sacheverells: Ralph (d.1539) with his wife occupies a recess in the N wall, their effigies under a low Gothic canopy still adorned with original gilding; Henry (d.1558) and his wife a tomb under the W bay of the chancel arcade; another Henry (d.1586) another tomb

Remains of Tudor **Rampton**

under the E bay. On the S wall stands a great alabaster monument to the third and last Henry Sacheverell of Ratcliffe (d.1625), with his three wives kneeling above him in canopied recess, surmounted by a cartouche of arms and crest. John Piper has portrayed these in a memorable picture, reproduced in the third volume of Sir Osbert Sitwell's autobiography, *Great Morning* (Macmillan & Co. 1948). In *Tales my Father Taught Me* (Hutchinson, 1962) Sir Osbert has described a

pilgrimage with his father and brother to the tombs of their Sacheverell ancestors at Ratcliffe, Barton-in-Fabis and Morley (Derbyshire): 'The three days', he writes, 'were a series of triumphant anti-climaxes ... When we reached what should have been the culmination of our pilgrimage, the church of Ratcliffe-on-Soar, we found the floor of the sacred edifice under water, to the height of half a foot. It was impossible to examine the series of tombs closely without wading, but from the door they looked, it must be admitted, impressive and beautiful. Four or five great rectangular masses, fashioned of Nottinghamshire alabaster and Derbyshire marble, bearing on them the recumbent effigies of knights and their ladies, seemed to float on a flat mirror of water ... My father refused to be depressed, and merely called to Robins, who was in attendance outside: "Robins, another time remember to put in my gumboots!"'

Rempstone [14] On the very southernmost edge of the county, close to the Leicestershire border, and with wide view S towards the high uplands of Charnwood Forest. The chubby little 18th-century *Church* stands by the side of the main road surveying the prospect; it has big Georgian windows, a battlemented, pinnacled tower, and an interior remarkably intact with box pews and two-decker pulpit. *Rempstone Hall*, a late Georgian (1796) two-storeyed white-painted brick house, turns its back to the road. It has passed through various hands, and is now the Mother House of the Community of the Holy Cross, a contemplative Anglican Benedictine order, founded in 1857 by Miss Elizabeth Neale, sister of Dr J.M. Neale, the hymnologist and founder of the famous convent at East Grinstead. The Holy Cross Community was first established in East London, under the guidance of Father Lowder of St Peter's London Docks; in 1886 it moved to Haywards Heath, and from there to Rempstone in 1980.

Retford [5] is an ancient market town: it received its first charter in 1246, and grew in importance in the 18th century when the Great North Road was diverted through it (1766) and when the Chesterfield Canal was constructed later in the century; the coming of the railway in the middle of the 19th century brought new industry and resulted in much Victorian building. The River Idle, running through the middle of the town, divides East Retford from West: both are ancient parishes. The best approach is by the road from Worksop (A620), past the plantations of Babworth and the long wall of West Retford Hall: the road descends, the tower and spire of the two ancient churches come in sight, and we arrive in the *Square*. This is dominated by the Victorian *Town Hall* (1866 by Bellamy and Hardy), a building of some magnificence, with bulging mansard roof and cheerful clock tower; there are one or two good 18th-century houses, the offices of Henry Spencer & Sons (the Sotheby's or Christie's of the North) and the *White Hart* with its courtyard; Cannon Square to the NE leads to the *Parish Church* of St Swithin (East Retford), a dignified cruciform building with lofty central tower. Outwardly the church appears all Perp: in fact a glance at some of the details reveals that it is an interesting 17th-century rebuilding of a medieval church. The tower fell in 1651 and the rebuilding was completed in 1658. Inside, the nave arcades are in part 14th century; the arches at the crossing are low and lead into a long chancel, with elaborate reredos by G.G. Place, who restored the church in 1855. There is much good Victorian glass: the central panel of the E window is by O'Connor, the rest by Clayton and Bell; there are also windows by Hardman, Wailes and Kempe. The N transept has an E aisle (Lady Chapel) rebuilt by Bodley in 1873, when the original arches, blocked up in the 17th century, were uncovered. In *Churchgate* (W end of church) stands Sloswick's Almshouse (founded 1657), an engaging little early 19th-century Gothick building; opposite, but concealed by other buildings, is a delicious little white-stuccoed Gothick house, decorated, it would seem, with icing sugar. In Chapelgate (S side of church) the *Old Sun Inn* is a low, stuccoed, timbered 16th-century hostelry. Bridgegate (N of the Square) leads to *St. Michael's*, West Retford— across the bridge over the River Idle. This is also an interesting church, with a distinguished 14th-century crocketed spire, with broaches below the parapet and little flying buttresses;—by Butterfield, whose brother was Rector here (note memorial in chancel).; inside there is a delicate Perp S arcade, with highly decorative niche on E pier containing figure of St Oswald; Victorian N arcade, and Victorianized Dec chancel. St. Michael's is a celebrated Anglo-Catholic shrine, and the richly furnished interior is full of atmosphere. To the S of the church it is a surprise to find in *Rectory Road* a farm, here in the middle of Retford! Beyond is *West Retford Hall*, a long, early 18th-century house of two storeys with sash windows, standing in its little park; formerly the home of the Huntsman family, the house is now flats, and the park is a public park. Opposite is Holy Trinity Hospital, in spiky Perp by Blore (1852 and later); West Retford House is a tall, square, late 18th-century house, now an hotel, and opposite the (1950s) RC church, Protestant Place leads into Queen Street, an area of large Victorian town houses, and so to the station. Walking across the park, we again reach the Square: on the E side Grove Street contains some good 18th-century houses, and at the far end an imposing Wesleyan Chapel of 1880; Carolgate (to the S) is now pedestrianized, but leads on, over the canal, to King Edward VI Grammar School, founded in 1552, and rebuilt in 1855—Tudor, somewhat unexpectedly by Decimus Burton. St Alban's, near by, is a spacious stone church of 1901 by Hodgson Fowler and beyond, down London Road, large Victorian houses stand in spacious gardens. St Saviour's stands in Welham Road (the A620, continuing from Churchgate), an attractive Commissioners'-type

building of 1827, in yellow brick with tall Perp windows and tall W turrets (à la King's Chapel), and an interior with W gallery to fit. The vicarage next door is contemporary—latest Georgian with sash windows. To the SW Ordsall is an old village, but now incorporated in the town. *Ordsall Church* is a conspicuous landmark from the railway line, with its embattled and pinnacled Perp tower: the body of the church was much restored by T.C. Hine (1876)—the chancel higher than the nave, and incorporating a large E window filled with Kempe glass; 13th-century nave arcades; early 15th-century screen (tower arch); monument, with kneeling figure, to Samuel Bevercotes (1603), of an old local Papist family.

Rolleston [11] Riverside landscape, with the tall pinnacled Perp tower of the *Church* in command. There is herringbone masonry in the N aisle, a mutilated Saxon cross shaft, and a Norman S door; the base of the tower is Norman too. But the glory of the church is the EE nave: stand in the N aisle and look across to the S to admire the two spectacular arcades, the N with quatrefoil shafts and simple capitals, the S with clustered columns and delicate foliated tops; the clerestory is Perp, all finished off externally in finest ashlar. A beautifully furnished interior, too, with 17th-century woodwork and a number of small monuments. The building was sympathetically restored at the end of the 19th century by Hodgson Fowler of Durham, himself a native of Rolleston, where his father and grandfather were incumbents. There are red-brick cottages and farms of unsophisticated charm: Kate Greenaway, author and illustrator of Victorian children's books, spent much of her childhood here. West of the church the lane leads across the level crossing to the Southwell Racecourse; the road to the S, to Fiskerton, should not be missed: it

Ratcliffe-on-Soar

runs close to the river and commands a great prospect of the Trent in all its majesty.

Ruddington [14] A large satellite village, S of Nottingham, which grew in the early 19th century on the framework knitting industry: some old workshops survive in the little streets S of the church, and some old cottages. Later in the century Victorian houses began to appear, for Nottingham citizens: *Manor Park*, N of the church, was delightfully laid out with large black-and-white or brick-and-tile

houses (à la Norman Shaw); and there are a few early 19th-century mansions, such as Ruddington Hall, and South Manor. *The Hermitage*, E of the church, is a small ancient house, incorporating a medieval hall concealed by early 18th-century brickwork. The *Church* is large and expensive, rebuilt in 1887 by Bell and Roper of Manchester, with an embattled and many-pinnacled exterior and NW spire, which incorporates old work. The original parish church was at Flawford, between here and Plumtree; Ruddington was merely

its 'chapelry'. Flawford fell into disuse in the 18th century as the population migrated. Opposite the church is Sir Thomas Parkyns's school (1852): this Sir Thomas was the 5th baronet, descendant of the Wrestling Baronet of Bunny (q.v.), and lived at South Manor. There is a spirited cartouche over the doorway.

Rufford Abbey [8] Driving along the A614 from Ollerton, one sees a pretty Tudoresque lodge on the right, great baroque gates on the left; they are closed, but there is a glimpse of the ruin of a great house at the end of a long lime avenue. The approach to *the Abbey* is now by the estate road a little to the S: sombre, sad and beautiful, the ruin of this great mansion, built in soft pink stone above the 12th-century monastic undercroft, casts a magic spell. The porch stands across a balustraded causeway, the front door framed by barley sugar columns is locked, the room above the porch open to the sky. To the right, two Jacobean gables are a ruin, to the right again the higher gabled end, crowned with its cupola, is still intact and habitable. To the left of the porch are the great gaping windows of the hall; all else has gone—the state rooms behind the hall, the late 17th-century block to the N, Salvin's grand staircase, the chapel. The Cistercian Abbey of Rufford was founded in 1148 by Gilbert de Gant, Earl of Lincoln, as an offshoot of Rievaulx. At the Dissolution the abbey and its lands were granted to the 6th Earl of Shrewsbury, Bess of Hardwick's fourth husband; the church and most of the monastic buildings were pulled down, leaving only the undercroft of the lay brothers' quarters, and above and around this a great Elizabethan house was built. In the 17th century the place descended to Sir George Savile of Thornhill, Yorkshire, grandson of

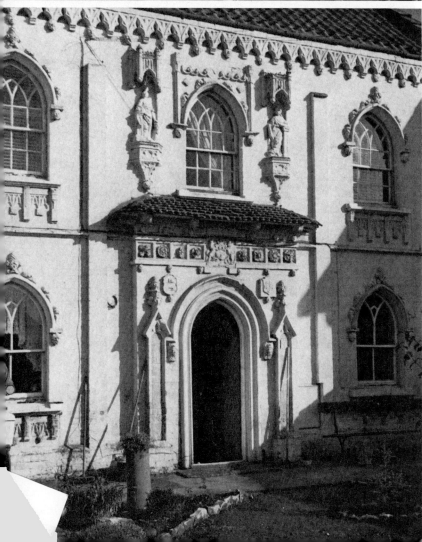

Retford: Sloswick's Gothick almshouse (*top*) and the sugar-iced version nearby

Bess of Hardwick's youngest daughter; his nephew was in turn created Viscount, Earl, and finally Marquis of Halifax; Royalist, politician, statesman, nicknamed 'The Trimmer', he it was who made the great 17th-century extensions to the house. The eventual Savile heiress married Richard Lumley, 4th Earl of Scarbrough (d.1782); three Earls of Scarbrough succeeded in turn, and the 8th Earl, when he died in 1856, unmarried, left five illegitimate sons by his French mistress. One of these, a distinguished diplomat, was created Lord Savile in 1888, but in 1938 the estate was sold, and the present Lord Savile lives on the family's estate in Yorkshire. After military occupation during the war, the house stood empty and crumbling for many years until purchased by the County Council; much of the house was pulled down in 1956, and what remains was placed in the care of the Ministry of Works. Restoration is in progress, but at present the ruins are not open to the public. *The Park*, however, is always open and much has been done in recent years to restore and re-create the landscape. To the S of the house stands the *Stable quadrangle*, a charming little courtyard of red brick, partly 17th, partly 19th century. This has been restored, and is used as an Art Gallery, where exhibitions are held in summer. Behind this, in a small walled garden, stands the *Bath House*, designed by John Hallam in 1729, with its Doric portico and two little towers, awaiting restoration. At the back it was aligned on the canal garden: the course of the old canal can still be traced, grassed over. It is a delight to walk through the gardens: there are spreading lawns and pleasant walks backed by old yew hedges. Behind are woodlands, intersected by the Broad Ride on the axis of the house, and to the E the great lake opens up, recently dredged and its banks

Retford: The eastern approach (*top*) and the Town Hall

replanted with trees. At the far end is a final pleasure: *the 18th-century Mill*—a delightful building of mellow brick, with stone quoins and cornice, sash windows and pediment; mill house and outbuildings adjoin, and the lane behind crosses a shallow ford, and makes for Wellow.

Saundby [6] The main road from Retford to Gainsborough twists and turns: the Hall Farm, the church tower embowered in cedars and great yews, a cottage *ornée* by the road, and a sprinkling of other houses. That is all there is of Saundby. The *Church* has to be approached through the barns and farm buildings of the Hall: there is a pinnacled Perp tower—indeed the church appears all Perp without; inside, an EE arcade, a little medieval glass under the tower, and many excellent windows by Kempe, and Clayton and Bell; a 14th-century effigy of a knight, an incised stone to William de Saundby (1418), rebuilder of the church, and a good Elizabethan tomb to Robert Helwys (d.1599), ancestor of the Lincolnshire family of Elwes. The chancel was tactfully rebuilt by Pearson in 1886, the N aisle by Weatherley in 1891. This beautiful little church was disgracefully abandoned ten years ago: it is hoped that help may soon be at hand (1983). Views from the churchyard across the Trent Valley: the mammoth power station at West Burton is an intimidating presence.

Scarle, South [9] A sequestered spot, approached by country lanes from Collingham or Besthorpe, or from the Lincolnshire frontier, so close at hand. (North Scarle is in that county: whence this discrimination?) Old cottages and farmhouses with their attendant buildings; one rather grander early Victorian house near the church— and that is all. The *Church* with its Nottinghamshire tower and unrestored exterior is a delight: the

pleasure is doubled on going inside and finding a spectacular Norman N arcade (related to that at South Collingham), an EE S arcade and chancel, an ancient roof, a double piscina, old pews with poppyheads, a medieval chancel screen, and an 18th-century vamping horn (a type of megaphone); monuments, too, including an incised slab to William Meyring (1510), and a series of minor later monuments, such as that (in white marble) to John Dalton, vicar (d.1769), 'an honest man's the noblest work of God' (Pope)—an unexpected, contemporary quotation.

Scarrington [11] The towers and spires and small villages of the Vale of Belvoir beckon to one another in their close proximity: Scarrington is such a one, with its plain, typically Notts, 14th-century spire, and little church largely rebuilt by J.H. Hakewill in the 1860s, but now held together inside by tie beams, and propped up externally on the N side. Outside the *Smithy* (SE of the church) is an extraordinary 'spire' formed of 50,000 horseshoes, standing as high as the smithy itself, which was built by the village blacksmith between 1945 and 1965. An attractive village.

Scofton [5] The A1 is not far away—Worksop and Manton colliery uncomfortably close. But Scofton is remote. A lane leads off the A620, crosses the Chesterfield Canal, and then the River Ryton: there are great farm buildings, a few cottages, and then the church, built in 1833 in the Norman style, by Ambrose Poynter. It is a building of some dignity, with nave and aisles and W tower; beautifully furnished interior; Foljambe monuments (note amusing details of the London house on tablet in sanctuary). From the churchyard there is a view of *Osberton Hall* across the lake, the home of the Foljambe family. The early tombs of the ancient family of Foljambe are at Chesterfield: they acquired

Osberton in the 18th century by marrying the heiress of the Thornhaghs (whose monuments are at Sturton-le-Steeple). The present house was built in 1806 by William Wilkins (junior): it was considerably enlarged by J. MacVicar Anderson in 1877; the stable courtyard is by Lindley of Doncaster. The estate is splendidly maintained, and the Osberton Horse Trials are held here every summer.

Screveton [11] (pronounced Screeton) The little villages of the Vale of Belvoir are all close neighbours: from the gently undulating ground at Screveton the brick tower of Hawksworth, the stone dovecote at Sibthorpe, the spires of Thoroton and Scarrington, Flintham Hall in its park, Belvoir itself on its hilltop, all seem very near; only a few fields divide Screveton from Car Colston. An informal grouping of red-brick cottages and farms; the Priest's House (1607), timber framed and tiny; a small *Church* almost dwarfed by its imposing, squat 15th-century tower, set in an immaculate churchyard—that is all there is, but it is just right. Inside, the church is simple and homely, with 13th-century arcades, pitch pine pews, and Hymns A & M; the Norman font has interlaced arcading, the priest's stall a 15th-century misericord, and the piscina in the S aisle unusual foliated carving; over the tower arch is a rare carved Charles II Royal Arms, and under the tower an interesting assemblage of monuments. The armoured figure of Richard Whalley (1583) occupies an elaborate alabaster tomb, his head and his feet supported on friendly whales, and three panels behind display his three wives and twenty-three children; there are two 17th-century Whalley monuments opposite, and a little 19th-century tablet commemorates Admiral Evelyn Sutton (1819), with a little piece of marble drapery below to his wife Roosilia (1829). Ancient trees to the W of the church mark

Shireoaks Hall

the site of the Hall, seat of the Whalleys from the time of Richard III to the late 17th century; an old picture shows a medieval manor house, with gabled porch and great hall, with 18th-century additions to right and left; Thomas Thoroton, brother of the antiquary (*see* Car Colston) acquired this from the Whalleys, and it remained the Thoroton home till they moved to Flintham in 1789. The old house was pulled down in 1823, its materials ignominiously used to bolster the Foss Way.

Scrooby [5] Bracing, open N Notts landscape with wide horizons: to the W the woods of Serlby Hall, to the N a distant glimpse of the great colliery at Harworth. The Old North Road runs on one side of the village (a quiet road now): the Great Northern main line on the other (by no means quiet). The *Church* has a distinctive and unusual 14th-century spire with crocketed pinnacles rising from the chamfered angles of the tower, and a battlemented parapet round its octagonal base; a battlemented Perp exterior, and a somewhat Victorianized interior. A cob from Plymouth Hoe (given by the late Sir Geoffrey Harmsworth) commemorates William Brewster, the Puritan leader, who gathered his Separatists here: the little party eventually set sail from Plymouth in the Mayflower in 1620, having obtained land in Virginia from Sir Edwin Sandys, the Governor. The small ledger stone near the S door to Penelope Sandys, granddaughter of the Archbishop of York whose tomb is in Southwell Minster, recalls the link between Sandys and Brewster; the former archiepiscopal manor house here was bequeathed by the archbishop to his son, and Brewster was in his service. Not far from the site of the great house *an ancient mill* straddles the river Ryton: a delectable spot.

Selston [10] Scarred industrial countryside. Wide views from the churchyard across the Erewash Valley to Alfreton and Pinxton: all the litter of industry—collieries, factories, run-down railway lines, suburban housing. The church is the only relic of antiquity, and apart from the embattled tower the exterior is over-restored. The interior is ancient, but much scraped. Transitional arcades in the nave; Perp clerestory. The best thing is the tomb in the chancel to William Willoughby, who died in 1630, aged 21. There is a long inscription, no doubt composed by his widow: 'His noble ways blazoned his progeny, and proved him a right true born Willoughby'; it then breaks into verse: 'Yet left he ere he went / A pair of female babes / Besides his infant heir / A hopeful imp, a right young Willoughby'. Near by is a 12th-century incised slab to a priest, and a Royal Arms of George III (1815).

Shelford [11] The road descends from Radcliffe into the valley of the Trent: woods clothe the hills on either side, and the tall Perp tower of the church is prominent; there are lanes of warm red cottages and farms, and the *Chesterfield Arms* keeps alive the long connection of the village with the Stanhope family. A spacious, dignified *Church*, with lofty Dec arcades, and Dec traceried windows, but over-restored by Ewan Christian in 1876; 17th-century font; excellent Kempe E window. The best things in the church are in the Stanhope Chapel: on the sill of the E window stands the notable fragment of a Saxon cross, the Virgin and Child carved on one side, a winged angel on another. Propped up near by is a baffling notice: 'Primitive Methodist Chapel 1840'; and under the window is the earliest of the many Stanhope monuments—to Anne, widow of Sir Michael Stanhope, who was granted Shelford Priory at the Dissolution by Henry VIII, but who had the misfortune to be be-

Sibthorpe

headed with Sir Thomas Arundel in 1552; she died in 1587. Her great grandson was created Earl of Chesterfield in 1628 and his first wife has a pretty monument, all draperies and swags, near by; she died in 1636: 'this small monument is dedicated to ye memory of his deare mother by Arthur Stanhope, her youngest son, who hath done ye like in ye church of St Giles in ye suburbs of London' (no doubt St Giles-in-the-Fields). There are many other memorials, including a Nollekens to Mrs Ellis (wife of the statesman, Welbore Ellis, and daughter of Sir William Stanhope), 1761, and a Chantrey to Lady Georgiana West (daughter of the 5th Earl), 1828. At the W end of the church a winding lane leads down to the river, where there are views

across to Stoke Bardolph on the opposite bank. To the E a long straight lane runs close to the river to Gunthorpe Bridge, and passes the old home of the Stanhopes, *Shelford Manor*, a venerable, patched-up pile, with blocked-up, mullioned windows—later sashes— and great barns and buildings, some old gatepiers, and other 17th-century features. The great house was built on the site of the Priory and was besieged by the Roundheads in 1745; after the Civil War the family moved to their new great house at Bretby (Derbyshire). Shelford descended to farmhouse status.

Shelton [12] A small secluded village in the back lanes near the River Devon. There is a plain, stuccoed early 19th-century Hall, with three storeys of sash windows and deep overhanging eaves; the *Manor House* has an 18th-century brick front and an elegant staircase inside; there are one or two good farmhouses, a sprinkling of cottages, and a little church with double bellcote. From the porch is a view across the meadows to copses and Belvoir beyond—all delightfully pastoral. The *Church* has a Norman doorway, Saxon fragments, 13th-century arcade and much-repaired ancient screen. On the W pier, the pretty armorial cartouche to William Warburton is 17th century; elsewhere small memorials to the Banks Wright family, squires and squarsons, who lived at the Hall till 1950: one 'lost two fingers at Viterbo in the Making of Italy' (1860); another, described as a 'Champion Public School Boxer' died of heat apoplexy in India (1894); the tasteful Victorian E window is inscribed 'Lydia Wright pinxit' (1863); the fragmentary panel in the W window bears the inscription 'To Lydia from her brother Vere'. The quintessence of Victorian life.

Shireoaks [5] A railway station on the line from Worksop to Sheffield, a mining village, the NW suburbs of Worksop. The great Shire Oak, which John Evelyn saw and measured (94 ft in girth), which marked the spot where Notts, Derbs and Yorks meet, is long since dead. The colliery was opened in 1845 by the 4th Duke of Newcastle (who had bought Worksop in 1839 from the Duke of Norfolk); his son built the *Church* in 1861, the architect T.C. Hine. Imposing exterior with transepts and central tower; inside, lofty crossing with angel corbels to carry the arches of the tower, a lofty nave with iron screen leading into lofty apsidal chancel, and a sanctuary glowing with mosaics and marble. A brass plate records the laying of the foundation stone by the Prince of Wales, in the presence of the Duke and Mr Gladstone: it is one of the greatest 19th-century

The Easter sepulchre, **Sibthorpe** (detail)

churches in the county—and too little known. The Duke built the long row of miners' cottages on the N side of the church, but many modern windows spoil what was an attractive design. But the special interest of the place is *Shireoaks Hall*, which stands to the W surveying open countryside. From the N, from the lane that leads to Thorpe Salvin, there is a glimpse of the house across its ponds and decaying park—a tall, gaunt, mutilated fragment; from the S, from the lane that leads past Steetley Chapel, there is a more distant view, of the battered W front with its rows of sash windows, many of them blocked up; as the lane twists, a wooden gate leading into a ploughed field marks the spot where the early 18th-century gatepiers, now at Clumber, once stood. The approach now is farther on, close to the farm buildings, and leads to the S front. This again is a fragment, a towering fragment, with enormously tall, blocked-up, mullioned windows, and a garden door on the ground floor. Shireoaks was acquired in 1546 by Thomas Hewett, a London merchant, and brother of Sir William, Lord Mayor, whose daughter married Edward Osborne, ancestor of the Dukes of Leeds, of nearby Kiveton Park (Yorkshire). Thomas's son, Henry Hewett, built the house c.1600, and his architect was almost certainly Robert Smythson. So much has been pulled down, so much altered, that it is not easy to imagine the house as it originally was. The front door was above the present garden door on the S front, and led into the great hall on the *piano nobile*; the state rooms would have been at the top, as at Hardwick, lit by the great windows now blocked. The builder's grandson was Sir Thomas Hewett, Surveyor General to George I: of his work here much remains. He refitted the house inside, built the two little stable blocks on the N front, and laid out the great gardens, which through all the changes since have miracu-

lously survived. In 1810 the last Hewett sold the property to the Duke of Norfolk (of near-by Worksop Manor); it was his agent, Mr Froggatt, who pulled down much of the building, and within the walls formed most of the present rooms. The W front, with its three storeys of sash windows, reflects the changed floor levels: it is not quite symmetrical, and the top windows are all blind—as are several on the first floor—so that even here the house wears a romantic, silent, withdrawn air. For a century and more it was used as a farmhouse, more recently as a potato store. It was in this pathetic state when discovered by Mr Leopold Godlewski, the architect (then an architectural student), who with his family has initiated a rescue operation, and reawakened the spirit of Shireoaks. Shireoaks is unique: *Sir Thomas Hewett's water gardens*, like the house, have survived by neglect. On the axis of the W front, beyond the bowling green, a long canal, still filled with water and followed by a succession of thirty-four cascades, disappears into the wood to end in a circular pool. Sir Thomas's radiating avenues await replanting, but restoration of the water garden has begun. On the N side of the house are two square pools, part of a formal layout; on the E side steps still lead down to a walled garden; and within the boundary wood is another pool—with the fragment of an 18th century pipe and nozzle to feed its fountain. Only the submerged cellars and foundations remain of the little *tempietto* which Sir Thomas built for banquets—adorned with painted ceilings and a bust of Sir Thomas by Rysbrack—but this will no doubt in time be rebuilt. For Shireoaks and its garden, so long forgotten and abandoned, this is the second spring.

Sibthorpe [11] In charming flat meadows, watered by the River Devon: a diminutive brick-built village, with two or three good

farmhouses, capacious farm buildings, and a cluster of cottages and newer houses. Church and medieval dovecote stand on the edge of the village, relics of a college of priests founded here in the 14th century to pray for the souls of the de Sibthorpes; in its heyday the college comprised a warden, nine priests, and two clerks. The *Church* is surrounded by a venerable circle of enormous Irish yews. There is a W tower of beautiful lias limestone; an 18th-century porch leads into an 18th-century flat-ceilinged nave: the Dec windows have been re-inserted in the blocked-up N arcade, and a lofty chancel arch leads into the grand 14th-century chancel, the choir of the college. Light pours through the great curvilinear windows; there is an arched recess for the founder's tomb, and above it is a small but elaborate Easter sepulchre, with two sleeping Roman soldiers below and the figure of the Risen Christ above. Against the N wall stands the alabaster tomb of Edward Burnell (d.1589), of the family (*see* Winkburn) who bought the property after the Dissolution and built a mansion here, of which nothing survives; cherubs hold a shield beneath the effigy; wreaths surround another shield above it. It is a Renaissance tomb of great beauty. Font of 1662, of the local school. In the field near by stands the great *14th-century stone dovecote*, tall and round, with a conical roof—curiously French in its character and appeal, romantic in its isolation.

Skegby [7] Mutilated countryside W of Mansfield: housing estates accompany the main road; there is a background of collieries and industry. A few old buildings are left in what was a country village—a tall, brick, late 18th-century house at the crossroads; *Skegby Hall* below, an earlier 18th-century building of brick with stone quoins and top parapet, once the home of the Lindley family, now a Notts County Council school: near by are the

Archbishop's Palace, **Southwell**

fragmentary ruins of their earlier manor house, a few stone walls with blocked up windows; and Manor Farm across the fields, a small gabled 17th-century house. The *Church* is in origin 13th century, but much rebuilt in 1870 as a result of mining subsidence: there are one or two monuments to the Lindleys, an E window by Kempe, and two early 14th-century effigies of a forester and his wife, now standing erect against the W wall. She wears a wimple and long gown: he carries a hunting horn. They are delightfully evocative of medieval Sherwood.

Sneinton, *see* Nottingham

Sookholme [8] As endearing as its name: a tiny Norman chapel in a field, a farmhouse or two, no village—but Warsop Vale colliery, with its smudge of miners' houses is not far away to the N: to the W Shirebrook colliery rears its mighty head. But Sookholme is a different world. The little *Chapel* has no tower, no bellcote—just a Norman chancel arch, a simple 14th-century sedile, some Dec or Perp windows, a Norman font, and that is all. Frontier country, close to the Derbyshire border.

South Clifton, *see* Clifton, South

South Collingham, *see* Collingham, South

South Leverton, *see* Leverton, South

South Muskham, *see* Muskham, South

South Scarle, *see* Scarle, South

South Wheatley, *see* Wheatley, South

Southwell [11] (pronounced Suth'll) The Cathedral of Nottinghamshire: a little town of exquisite charm: a jewel among English cathedrals. Southwell is remarkably unknown—even among connoisseurs; it is also remarkably unexpected. Approach it from Newark, leaving a fair-sized town behind—suddenly, and before long, just beyond Upton, *the Minster* comes in sight, and then the little town; indeed, approaching it from anywhere, the sense of surprise is one of the ingredients of Southwell's charm. The spires suddenly, unexpectedly, appear, a great church in what appears to be little-more than a large village. Southwell is also unusual: the lead spires, those 'Rhenish caps', are unique in England; you might almost be in the Rhineland. And Southwell is unspoiled: stand by the great church, survey the prebendal houses, walk up the narrow streets; there is hardly a jarring building. The Philistines have never been here: long may they be kept at bay. The manor of Southwell was given by King Eadwig to Oskytel, Archbishop of York in 956. A century later a college of priests, or prebendaries, had been established here, and from then on the Minster of Southwell served as a kind of sub-cathedral in the great archdiocese of York, just as Ripon did in the West Riding, and Beverley in the East. The prebendaries (or canons) had a prebendal house in Southwell named after the village in which their estates were: there were prebendaries of Rampton and Oxton, Muskham and Normanton, three prebendaries of Norwell, and so on; they took turns to come into residence at Southwell, though a few would always be in residence;

at other times vicars choral would deputize for them. The collegiate foundation survived the Reformation, survived until 1841 when it was abolished; but the last Prebendary of the old foundation did not die until a few years before the foundation of the new Diocese of Southwell on 2 February 1884, when the Minster became its cathedral; but it had always been the mother church of Notts. The Archbishop of York had *a palace* of which extensive ruins remain, on

the S side of the Minster; a new house was formed within the walls (by W.D. Caroe) for the Bishop of Southwell in 1904. Approach the great church from the W, absorb the austere *Norman W front*, the lead-capped towers, the great Perp W window; enter and survey the Norman nave built in the early 12th century. With its plain drum pillars and round arches, the wide arches of the triforium, and smaller arches of the clerestory, the arcades are somehow reminiscent of the great

The west front

◁ The nave, **Southwell**

Roman aqueducts of southern
France. Beyond the screen there is
a glimpse of the EE chancel. Walk
up the nave, and stand under the
central tower; the transepts are
Norman too, *the chancel screen* one of
the greatest triumphs of the Dec
style; through the tall narrow entry
there is the most superb view into
the choir: a magnificent 18th-
century brass candelabra, an early
16th-century brass lectern, and
above the high altar *four lancets* filled
with 16th-century French glass,
whose gorgeous colours illuminate
the E end and make an unforgettable impression. Now it is time to
enter the chancel and absorb the
elegant EE arcades, the long lancet
windows, the elegant rib vaulting.
The E side of the screen is still richer
than the W: the carved leaves, the
carved heads, the intricate pattern-
ing of niches and arches; above the
entry the three little statues have recently been gilded. *The chancel* with
its clustered columns is a wonderful
foil for the solid severity of the Norman nave. The French glass,
rescued from the Temple Church in
Paris, was presented to the Minster
by Henry Gally Knight, MP for the
county and a distinguished antiquary, in 1818. On the S side of the
sanctuary is the moving figure of
Bishop Ridding '43rd Head Master
of Winchester, 1st Bishop of Southwell, Ruler, Scholar, Divine'; He
died in 1904. The bronze figure is
by F.W. Pomeroy, the base by
Caroe. The upper E windows are
by Clayton and Bell (1876); in the
aisles there is interesting early glass
by Kempe (1876). Two low E transepts open out of the chancel, and
from the N aisle a short enclosed
cloister leads to the *Chapter House*,
the great climax of a visit to Southwell, its greatest and most glorious
surprise. Built at the very end of the
13th century, it is the greatest

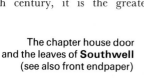

The chapter house door
and the leaves of **Southwell** ▷
(see also front endpaper)

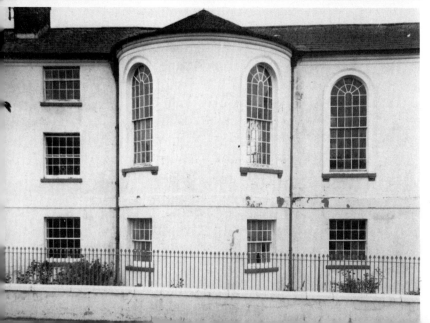

achievement in England of the Dec style, 'among chapter houses as the rose amongst flowers': the elegant doorway, with its one slender central column, and marble shafts at the sides, the wealth of carvings in the capitals and the arch itself, leads into the Chapter House. The vaulting is unsupported by any central pier, the great traceried windows, filled with clear glass in which fragments of medieval glass are set, flood the building with light. Below the windows, the arcades, which provide shallow canopies for the canons' seats are decorated with an incredible wealth of carved foliage—*the leaves of Southwell*. Thirty years ago Sir Nikolaus Pevsner produced a King Penguin volume so entitled, entirely devoted to these carvings: alas, that it has long been out of print, but extracts were read at the Memorial service after his death (1983). Returning to the N transept, one may note the 11th century tympanum (from the earlier, Saxon, church) over the small doorway; also the alabaster tomb of Archbishop Sandys (d.1588), showing him in eucharistic vestments as though a pre-Reformation prelate—but with his children's figures below. Near by is the attractive bust of Sir Edwyn Hoskyns, 12th Bt and 2nd Bishop of Southwell (d.1925) by Reynolds Stephens. In the S transept is the Royal Arms of Charles II. Here the S door leads out to the Palace: alternatively it may be preferred to leave the church by the N porch (noting the interesting 17th-century font on the way)—a magnificent Norman porch, with a barrel-vaulted roof. From here we can compass the entire S side: there is a good view of the Palace; in the ruined E parts a charming garden has been made. Passing the E end

Southwell
Rampton Prebend
Cranfield House
Baptist Chapel

we come to *Vicars' Court*, an enchanting little open quadrangle of Georgian houses, built about 1780 to house the vicars choral, with the Residence at the E end, built on the site of the medieval Vicars' Hall. Until 1841 the canon in residence came to stay here for his period 'in residence'; the house was kept furnished and heated for whichever prebendary it might be. It is now the provost's residence; the four smaller houses are occupied by two residentiary canons, the vicar choral, and the rector chori. Former prebendal houses stand on the other side of Church Street: the most distinguished is Cranfield House (Oxton Prebend), built in the very early 18th century, with its stone dressings and hipped roof. Normanton Prebend is a tall, late 18th-century house with fine gatepiers; South Muskham Prebend is gabled and in origin medieval, but Georgianized with sash windows and stucco. A short walk down Easthorpe reveals more 18th- (or early 19th-)century houses and cottages—one or two with cast-iron balconies. *The Bramley Apple* recalls the discovery of this excellent apple in Mr Bramley's orchard near here in 1805: it is much cultivated in Southwell. From the end of the street there is a splendid view back, with the E end of the Minster rising above the red-brick houses. There is a footpath beside Normanton Prebend, which leads up behind these houses to Burgage Lane: here there are large Georgian houses— Hill House and Burgage Court— fine, stylish buildings, and we can walk on to the Burgage itself, the long green which descends the hill to the N. Here there are several delightful Georgian houses: *Burgage Manor* at the top is the house which Byron's mother occupied when her

The Saracen's Head
Byron's House
Greet House: 1824 workhouse
over the river to the east

Stanford-on-Soar

son first inherited Newstead (but which they were too impoverished to occupy). At the foot of the green is the House of Correction with its portentous arched entrance (by Richard Ingleman, 1807). Back into the centre of the town through King Street we find the *Saracen's Head* with its timbered front, and long yard through the archway, with more black-and-white timbering. Westgate continues, with many good houses: opposite the Minster Gateway is the *Rampton Prebend*, the most endearing of all the prebendal houses. Its three gables betray its 16th- or early 17th-century origin; the Georgians stuccoed the front and inserted sash windows. It is a building of special charm, and from the dining room window there is an unforgettable view across the garden to the great church standing serene and dominant above the yew

trees and the medieval gateway. There are many houses to enjoy in Westgate: round the corner in the road to Nottingham is the large, early 19th-century cream-washed Baptist chapel with its enormous bow—a building of charm. Westgate continues to Holy Trinity (by Hadfield, 1844) with its tall broach spire; beyond is the quiet street called Westhorpe, with the early 19th-century Westhorpe Hall standing hidden in its large garden and little park beyond. In Queen Street there are more houses to enjoy: Norwood Villas is an unexpected Victorian newcomer (1877). And along the road to Halam is *Norwood Park*. Originally one of the Archbishop's hunting parks, Norwood was acquired by the Sutton family in 1764. John Sutton, bachelor great great grandson of a younger brother of Lord Lexington (*see*

Averham), built the house forthwith; he was succeeded by his brother Sir Richard, MP and Lord of the Treasury, who was created a baronet in 1772; Sir Richard, 2nd Bt, was the famous sportsman who appears in John Ferneley's great picture of the Burton Hunt, now in the Usher Gallery at Lincoln. The Starkey family acquired the place in 1881; Sir John (1st Bt and MP for Newark) started the fruit farming here, for which Norwood is now famous. The rose-red Georgian house, with its pedimented centre and lower wings, standing on its terrace, faces SE towards the Minster. The architect is unknown; but the great ancient trees, the young fruit trees climbing the slopes, a classical temple on a hill, a little garden house at the end of a vista, the plantations of black poplars, all combine to make a setting of great delight.

The centenary of Southwell was celebrated in 1984, one of the highlights of which was the presentation by the Queen of the Royal Maundy money on Maundy Thursday.

Stanford-on-Soar [17] The very southernmost tip of the county, watered by the River Soar, the King's Brook, and the Grand Union Canal. There is little 'village': one or two good-looking groups of cottages of the 17th or early 19th century, a white-stuccoed manor house, the disused Great Central Railway line (Marylebone–Nottingham) accompany the *Church*. This is handsome, with embattled Perp W tower: a great restoration by W.S. Weatherley (1892) created the High Victorian, High Church interior we see today; it is distinguished and devout, with ornate rood screen and figures, the wall above the chancel arch decoratively stencilled. The chancel is more or less a rebuilding by Weatherley. Old photographs show the building before restoration: an angel (in plaster no doubt) blowing a trumpet stands above the chancel arch, a similar figure above the tower arch. One cannot but regret their banishment. There is a brass in the chancel to a vested priest (*c*.1400), and the E end of the S aisle is occupied by the raised vault of the Lewes and Dashwood families, lords of the manor from the 17th to the 19th century. There is a handsome marble monument with garlands and cherubs to Thomas Lewes (d.1694), Alderman of London, who acquired the manor: his daughter and granddaughter married Dashwoods of Kirtlington (Oxon), the younger son and grandson of Sir Robert Dashwood, 1st Bt. There are later monuments to Dashwoods: Samuel Vere Dashwood was squarson for nearly 50 years. Stanford Hall (now Co-operative College) was built for Charles Vere Dashwood in 1771 by William Henderson of Loughborough, in a very fine position up the hill to the NE commanding the great view towards Charnwood Forest. In origin a restrained brick house with curving wings and little external ornament, it was much embellished by later owners, especially Sir Julien Cahn, who built a private theatre here. The house has been much added to by the college, but the park remains beautiful.

Stanton-on-the-Wolds [14] If one approaches from the E, from the Foss Way, on the A606 (Melton Mowbray–Nottingham), the wolds seem remote and there are grand views in all directions, especially across the Vale of Belvoir. Stanton became a tiny village as the wolds became depopulated in the 18th century. The little *Church* was almost abandoned—to be restored and revived in the late 19th century by Mrs Robertson of Widmerpool. It is an endearing little medieval chapel, with well-buttressed sloping S wall, unusual little pepperpot turret for the bell, and immaculate interior. It is approached by a track behind an old farmhouse. To the W modern residential housing almost links the place with Keyworth.

Stapleford [13] A *Saxon Cross*, a pair of ornamental iron gates originally at Wellington College, and a long line of Swithland slate slabs banked along the churchyard path, are the three contrasting and unexpected features which greet the visitor. The Cross is the most important pre-Conquest monument in the county: the tall shaft is adorned with intricate carving, which includes a winged eagle standing on a serpent, perhaps denoting St Luke. An interesting *Church*, too, chiefly of the 13th and 14th centuries: the Dec E window with its intersecting tracery is filled with glass by Mayer of Munich (1876); the SE Chapel is a posthumous work by Sir T.G. Jackson (1925)—remarkably harmonious; and there are many monuments. The incised slab to Robert Tevery (1553) near the chancel step is now unfortunately concealed by the platform for a nave altar; there is a large alabaster monument in the S aisle to Gervase Tevery (1639); near the S door is a tablet adorned with sphinxes to George Borlase Warren, killed at Aboukir Bay (1801), son of Sir John Borlase Warren, the admiral; and the monument to 'Thomas Gray of Nottingham, Gent' (1802) describes his benefactions to the neighbourhood and kingdom as 'the Improver of roads and Pioneer of mail coaches'. Stapleford Hall, now demolished, was the home of the Warrens: old photographs depict it as an odd, mildly Gothick, late 18th-century house, with an octagonal conservatory in front looking like a bandstand on a sea front. Stapleford was a village of lace factories and frameworkknitters' houses; there are still terraces of *knitters' cottages* to be seen (e.g. in Nottingham Road). The old main road twists and turns through the place, crossing the railway, the River Erewash, the Erewash Canal, and finally landing in Derbyshire.

Staunton-in-the-Vale [12] for antiquity: a glimpse of an ancient house across the park, the *Staunton Arms* at the crossroads, proclaim the presence of the Stauntons of Staunton, Nottinghamshire's very oldest family—indeed perhaps the oldest family in England still to inhabit the ancestral estate from which they take their name. The Stauntons have been at Staunton since 1041, and are still here. A visit to the *Church* standing close to the *Hall* emphasizes their antiquity, their tenacity in holding on. Most of the church is 14th century (sympathetically restored in 1853 by E.J. Willson of Lincoln) with a prominent tower with low pyramid roof standing at the E end of the N aisle. The nave is light and spacious; the chancel, protected by an early 16th-century screen, is darker, with rich Victorian glass. The N aisle, as spacious as the nave, called the St Laurence Choir, is filled with

Staunton monuments; there are more in the chancel. At the W end of the aisle is a marble tablet by Westmacott (1811) to Job Staunton Charlton, MP for Newark, whose grandmother, the inscription tells us, was daughter of Harvey Staunton Esq., 'whose ancestors inherited the Estate here from the time of the Saxons'; it goes on to describe how Sir Mauger Staunton defended Belvoir Castle against 'William Duke of Normandy, commonly called the Conqueror'. That puts history in its right perspective: the Stauntons have seen dynasties rise and fall, governments come and go. Looking round, one sees few memorials of note to the Tudor or Elizabethan Stauntons (when most of our old families were getting going); only small tablets from the 17th or 18th centuries. The great monuments are to Stauntons of the 13th and 14th centuries—cross-legged knights in chain mail, ladies in the dress of the period: the Stauntons were important long before most of our important families—and they are still here. The author's ancestor John Thorold of Marston married a Miss Staunton in the reign of Henry VII: the families have called each other 'cousin' ever since. The house is clearly visible from the church, venerable and ancient; the porch is clearly 16th century (or earlier), with Tudor doorway, mullioned windows here, and to light the great hall; 18th-century bays with sash windows to right and left indicate Georgian improvements; the family was not wealthy enough at that time to pull down, and build a fashionable new house. Over the front door is an exceptionally fine carved coat of arms, erected by Robert Staunton in 1573, with the family motto 'Moderata Durant'—that is the secret of their survival. The house is not open to the public, but if we are invited in, and close the front door behind us, there will be seen bullet holes in the ancient door: '1645' is inscribed above each one. Colonel William Staunton raised a

Staunton Hall and early occupant

164

regiment of foot for Charles I and was present at the raising of the Royal Standard at Nottingham in 1642; Mrs Staunton stayed at home and fortified the house with pillows, bolsters and mattresses against the invader in 1645. At last she had to surrender. But the family came back. The great hall has been delightfully Georgianized; an 18th-century staircase occupies the screens passage. And walking out on to the terrace on the garden side we may see a great and *ancient beech tree*—the foliage and branches in the middle carefully cut back and trimmed: through this opening will be seen Belvoir Castle. The Stauntons originally held the manor in return for the duty of castleguard: in an emergency they were to rush to the rescue of the Castle with armed men. The entrance tower at Belvoir is called the Staunton Tower, and whenever the Sovereign visits the Castle the Staunton of the day must be there to open the great door with a golden key. The beech tree is kept trimmed, so that even today the squire of Staunton can make sure that all's well at Belvoir. A short distance to the E on Folly Hill stands a small brick 18th-century cottage with tower attached, on the Notts–Lincs frontier: from here there is a wide view across the Vale into Lincolnshire and Leicestershire; near by the *Three Shire Bush* marks the point where the three counties meet. Mr Staunton has recently replanted the 'bush'—a chestnut specially grown on the estate, and he tends it carefully to make sure that no enemy, no boundary commissioner from London, should remove this landmark.

Stockwith, West [3] Nottinghamshire's most northerly outpost: a place of considerable charm. The River Idle, the Mother Drain, and the Chesterfield Canal all join the Trent here, and in the 17th and 18th centuries West Stockwith became an important little inland port with warehouses and boat-

building yards. Now it is a little faded, but the Canal basin is full of boats and barges and on the E bank of the Trent, opposite, stands East Stockwith—in Lincolnshire, and inaccessible except by boat—with its plain little Victorian church, and one delicious Gothick house: a delightful little stretch of stage scenery. The village street runs parallel with the Trent, with a small red-brick Georgian church on the river bank. Built in 1722 by the executors of William Huntington, 'ship carpenter', the simple interior is prettily adorned with elegant plaster and woodwork. William Huntington himself reclines on his tomb (by Edward Poynton of Nottingham), holding in his hand the design of a sailing ship—perhaps one of the sea-going ships built in his yard here.

Stoke, East [11] The Battle of Stoke took place here on 16 June 1487: the army of Henry VII routed the Yorkists, who were intent on putting the pretender Lambert Simnel on the throne. After three hours' fighting 7,000 men were slain: others fled to the river where the meadow—still called *the Red Gutter*—flowed with blood. Today the long brick wall of the park of Stoke Hall and the *Pauncefote Arms* at the crossroads are the landmarks on the Foss. The wall and a few cottages accompany the lane to the W; a bridge across the lane connects the walled gardens with the house, and steps lead up to the church. The lane leads on, down to the meadows by the Trent, to the Red Gutter, and a peaceful view of the *Bromley Arms* at Fiskerton opposite. The tower and chancel of the *Church* are medieval: the nave was rebuilt in 1738, and a Tuscan arcade divides nave from S aisle; there is a Victorian chancel arch, a little medieval glass, and a number of monuments to the Bromley family. A tablet in the S aisle commemorates Sir George Smith, 1st Bt (d.1769)—son of Abel, and grandson of Thomas

Smith, the founder of Smith's Bank (*see* Nottingham); his son, the 2nd Bt, assumed the name of Bromley, and in due course that of Pauncefote, families from whom he was descended through his mother and grandmother respectively; the descendant of the younger brother of the 1st Bt was the first Ambassador to the USA (1893–1902), and took the title of Lord Pauncefote. The Union Jack hanging in the nave came from the Washington Embassy, and he is buried in the churchyard, in a tomb surmounted by an angel, close to the tower. Admiral Arthur Bromley (later 8th Bt) took part in Scott's Antarctic Expedition (1911): a framed inscription under the tower commemorates the event. Handsome quadrangular stables stand behind the church: the house itself was built in 1812 by Lewis Wyatt, but incorporated older work. Much of the house was demolished after the departure of the Smiths (or Bromleys), after the First World War.

Stoke Bardolph [11] There is a small road that leads off the A612 near the railway bridge at Gedling—straight to Stoke Bardolph; but the more delightful way is to cross the railway near Burton Joyce station and take the road down to the Trent. This runs all the way along the river bank to the little hamlet of Stoke, where there is a small brick Gothic church of 1844, and a handful of houses. There are grand views up- and downstream, and across to Shelford on the opposite bank.

Stokeham [6] The flat empty countryside W of the Trent: inconsequential lanes lead in all directions. At a crossroads here stands the hamlet of Stokeham, with a homely little medieval church, which lost its S aisle in the 18th century; blocked arcade, mullioned windows with clear glass, EE and Dec windows elsewhere, and double bellcote. Views across to the

Rampton Asylum to the NW, and to the great power stations at Cottam and High Marnham to the E.

Strelley [10] On the very westernmost outskirts of Nottingham: past the vast housing estates of Bilborough the main road (A6002) forks left, and a country lane leads on to 'Strelley only'. A few estate cottages, and the lane turns, skirts the park, and church and hall come in sight. Splendid tower, splendid *Church*—all (except the base of the tower) built in pink Mansfield stone by Sir Sampson Strelley in the mid-14th century. A lofty nave leads to a lofty chancel, protected by perhaps the finest rood screen in the county, and containing the tombs of the powerful medieval family of Strelley. The recumbent figures of Sir Sampson and his wife, hands clasped, occupy the centre of the chancel, another alabaster tomb to John and his wife (1501) the N side of the sanctuary; there is an incised slab to John de Strelley (1421), and a double brass to Sir Robert and his wife (1487). The stalls are complete with misericords, and the sanctuary is beautifully furnished by C.G. Hare, who also decorated the S Chapel and restored the rood. The Strelleys, once so rich and powerful, sold out to the Edge family, Nottingham lawyers, in the 17th century, and finally petered out in the 18th; the S Chapel contains the modest ledger stones and monuments to the Edges—an interesting contrast. There is excellent Flemish glass (16th century) in the chapel, and there are medieval fragments in the nave. Across the churchyard wall stands *Strelley Hall*, built for Thomas Webb Edge by Thomas Gardner of Uttoxeter in 1789: of stuccoed brick, it stands foursquare, three storeys high, the E and S fronts pedimented; in fact the SW corner incorporates the medieval tower of the Strelleys, and there is a vaulted room inside; elsewhere there are handsome 18th-century interiors. The last Edge owner died in 1977: the park now belongs to Nottingham Corporation, and the house is used as offices.

Sturton-le-Steeple [6] Like a great, tall, square birthday cake with 12 candles round the rim, the great tower of Sturton with its 12 pinnacles is a grand spectacle here in the flat lands of NE Notts. 'Sturton' is a corruption of 'Stretton', or the town on the street—the Roman road known as Till Bridge Lane, which once crossed the Trent at Littleborough, and still runs on through Wheatley and Clayworth to join Ermine Street S of Doncaster. Apart from the tower, the church was burnt out in 1901. It was rebuilt by Hodgson Fowler on the original lines—but little survives except for the tragic scorched monuments, now tidied away under the tower: the largest (1687) is to the widow of Sir Richard Earle of Stragglethorpe (Lincolnshire); her daughter married John Thornhagh of Fenton (in Sturton parish). Two others are to her grandson, another John Thornhagh, MP, and his wife, a Savile of Rufford (1767); their daughter married Francis Foljambe of Aldwark, Yorkshire; the Foljambes still hold the estate (*see* Scofton).

Sutton Bonington [13] Leicestershire border country: the River Soar is the frontier. Two ancient churches, an attractive village street, the main Midland line rushing past in a cutting, the Nottingham University School of Agriculture, grand views towards Charnwood Forest. *St Michael's, Bonington*, has a tall 15th-century spire, a lofty nave with 13th- and 14th-century arcades, and a notable 14th-century font with projecting ledges (for book and candle) reminiscent of the font at Youlgreave in Derbyshire; bright Victorian glass in S aisle; sombre Kempe windows in chancel and N aisle; monument to 1st Lord Elton, author and broadcaster; a scraped interior. *St Anne's, Sutton*, is a small church up the hill to the S,

with bellcote and 13th-century features; another scraped interior, more Kempe glass. Two timber-framed houses in the street, and many attractive later houses: pride of place goes to the *Hall*, an early 18th-century house with pedimented doorway and sash windows, behind high walls and overlooking its own meadows on the other side of the road; a very handsome house. It was built by Beaumont Parkyns, brother of the Wrestling Baronet of Bunny (q.v.), and in the 19th century belonged to George Paget (director of the Midland Counties Railway) and his son Sir Ernest (chairman of the Midland). They had a private platform in the grounds, and trains were expected to slow down as they passed. *St Anne's Manor* with its Dutch Gables, on the high ground behind, was built in 1849 (by the Pagets), but largely rebuilt after a fire in 1908 (Barrowcliff and Alcock, architects): it has a garden of great beauty, commanding the magnificent view. *Zouch* is a little canal settlement on the navigable River Soar: an old mill, a lock near by, brightly painted barges tied up near the bridge.

Sutton-cum-Lound [5] Wide, flat, green country between Retford and Barnby Moor: there are low hills in the distance everywhere, and broad, sweeping views from rising ground anywhere. The Old North Road, the main railway line to Edinburgh, the Chesterfield Canal, all make their way, N or S, E or W across this level countryside. Twin villages: Sutton has the grand church, Lound the good houses. At Sutton imposing 18th-century gatepiers lead only to a Victorian house. But the *Church* is rewarding. Approaching from the E there is a fine grouping of lofty Perp tower, lofty Dec nave, lofty chancel; battlements and pinnacles abound, so do great Dec curvilinear windows. Spacious interior: the chancel arch is Norman (though somewhat restored), the rest Dec or Perp; a 15th-century screen in the

West Stockwith

chancel, some ancient pews, Royal Arms of George III (1799). Lound has a narrow street, with many decent brick houses and cottages; Lound Hall is tall and square, Georgian, and there is an attractive little Victorian brick church.

Sutton-in-Ashfield [7] is now somewhat soulless: all supermarkets and 'centres'; there is a shopping precinct called 'the Idlewell Centre', with the usual multiple shops, and a bus station, and behind that 'the Sutton Centre', with a comprehensive school and so-called 'leisure facilities' and a 'sports centre'. What does this word 'centre' mean? It is the centre of nothing. Almost nothing survives of the old place, a shabby but endearing overgrown village or little colliery town, but a few small 17th- or 18th-century houses. Vigorous pleas were made, but to no effect. Sutton has been the

victim of 'progress': it is now sad and anonymous. The church in its old churchyard, gloomy but full of atmosphere, the 19th-century rectory and school, surrounded by trees on the higher ground, seem marooned on their own: behind them a great sea of council houses, below them the old town now all torn apart. But there is 'character' here. The *Church* is well worth a visit: a plain 14th-century spire, rising from a battlemented tower; 13th-century arcades—one capital charmingly carved with leaves and human heads; some restoration in the 19th century; a few monuments. For the rest—it is but a huge subtopian sprawl.

Sutton-on-Trent [9] A metropolis among the Trentside villages, which become ever smaller and more obscure as the lanes leading N disappear into the unknown world of vast flat fields and vast tall

power stations beyond. Sutton is a village of many lanes, with the main railway line and the A1 dual carriageway roaring past near by. The *Old England Hotel* is a noted hostelry, established in the halcyon days of motoring before the war, when the Great North Road passed through the village. A distinguished *Church*: tower of three stages, originally crowned with a spire (taken down in 1830); the great glory is the Mering Chapel on S side of chancel; the view of the exterior from the SE builds up grandly with the battlemented nave, the large Perp windows, the pinnacles, the gargoyles—and the even richer ornament of the chapel. Inside, an exceptionally fine screen (*c.*1510) with overhanging loft leads into the chapel, and the Purbeck marble tomb of Sir William Mering; the Merings of Mering were an ancient family, long extinct; and Mering itself is long submerged in the watery meadows of the Trent. There are a few fragments of ancient glass, a window by Geoffrey Webb (1927), and some old stall ends in the chancel.

Syerston [11] The flat lands near Newark turn to gently undulating country as the Foss makes its way S, and steep wooded banks descend to the Trent on the W. Syerston Hall stands to the W of the main road, the village—little more than a handful of houses and the church—to the E. The *Church* has a narrow 13th-century tower, and a narrow, aisleless nave, intimate and charming, sympathetically restored in 1896; the pulpit is dated 1636, the squire's pew and chancel stalls are handsome Victorian. All monuments are to Fillinghams, from William (d.1795) to George (d.1974)—the latter by David Rowbotham. The Fillinghams, who were agents to the Dukes of Rutland, built up an estate here in the later 18th century; William built the *Hall* (1793), a perfect late Georgian brick house of two storeys, with hipped roof and stone porch, standing in its own small park. Behind the house, stables and dovecote form a harmonious informal quadrangle; behind them, magnificent farm buildings.

Teversal [7] The housing estates of Stanton Hill, the local collieries, the *Lucky Days Bingo Hall*, do not prepare you for the ancient secluded village: turn N at the *Carnarvon Arms*, dive under a series of railway bridges (for sidings which serve the mine at Silver Hill), and you are in a different world, a small village of stone houses and stone walls—in character a Derbyshire village; indeed the frontier is very near, and the park wall and ancient trees of Hardwick are clearly visible. The *Church* is a rare jewel—not so much for its architecture, though the notable Norman N door, the 12th-century arcades, and the 15th-century tower are all of interest—but for its sumptuous

Teversal

17th-century fittings, its monuments, and its hatchments. There are box pews throughout: the squire's pew is on a raised dais, with canopy supported on barley sugar pillars. The earliest monuments are the incised slabs to Roger Greenhalgh (1563) and his wife, a Babington of Dethick (1538); their granddaughter married Francis Molyneux of Hawton (q.v.), and Teversal remained with the Molyneux till the death of the last baronet, and subsequently with the Earls of Carnarvon, who succeeded by marriage, till 1929; there are excellent 17th- and 18th-century monuments to the Molyneux

baronets in the chancel—to Sir Francis, 2nd Bt (1674) 'qui patrimonium familiae, familiae patrimonium reliquit et adauxit'; to Sir John, 3rd Bt (1691) and his wife, and Sir Francis, 4th Bt and his wife (1741); finally Sir Francis, Kt and Bt (1812) 'Gentleman Usher of the Black Rod during the long period of 47 years ... the 7th and last Baronet of this ancient family.' There are seven hatchments, the most recent being that of the Countess of Carnarvon (1876), wife of the 3rd Earl, and heiress of the Molyneux family. Cushions embroidered with the Molyneux arms adorn the family pew, where the

Molyneux monument, **Teversal**

first was built in 1685, and is usually ascribed to Talman (the evidence is not conclusive). Pictures survive of a mansion of red brick with stone dressings, a long front of three storeys, the top balustraded and capped with urns. It was built for the 4th Earl of Kingston, and was destroyed in a fire of 1745. The second, designed by John Carr, was a compact red-brick house, with stone base and Ionic columns, built in 1767. A century later it was felt to be altogether too insignificant for the 3rd Earl Manvers, who was determined to erect something worthy of his ancient and distinguished family: this is what Salvin produced. All the great families of the Dukeries were related to each other: all were descended from Bess of Hardwick. But only the Pierreponts were an indigenous, ancient, Nottinghamshire race, for centuries seated at Holme Pierrepont (q.v.). Robert Pierrepont, 1st Earl of Kingston-upon-Hull, acquired Thoresby in 1633; the 4th Earl enclosed the park, and built the house of 1685 (perhaps incorporating part of an earlier house); the 5th was created Duke of Kingston by George I. But the Thoresby dukedom was short lived: the 2nd and last Duke was succeeded by a nephew, Charles Meadows, who assumed the name of Pierrepont, and in 1807 was created Earl Manvers. The new house was begun in 1865: it is one of the great Victorian houses of England. The entrance is on the E front, where the great pile of the house rises through five storeys and is crowned with clock tower and cupola. This recalls Harlaxton, but Harlaxton was built 30 years before; here at Thoresby (as Victorian taste dictated) the composition is no longer symmetrical, nor is the longer S front. Elaborate windows, elaborate chimneys, elaborate ornament everywhere—a big tower here, a smaller tower there, all lavishly decorated, the design lacks some of the subtlety and assured serenity of Harlaxton; but it is unquestionably

Carnarvons' prayer books still remain in their places, as though the family were expected in church next Sunday: 'Elsie Carnarvon, with much love, December 1878' reads the inscription in one of them. The Manor House lies to the SW, an ancient house Jacobethanized by Burn in 1896; the Old Rectory near the church is 17th century. Time has moved slowly at Teversal.

Thoresby [8] On the drive N from Ollerton up the long, straight A614, the presence of a great domain is soon apparent: first come the *Buck Gates* with their lodge, then a church spire in the park away to the left, estate cottages, the Palladian archway of the *Old Kennels*—and then, above the plantations, a flag flying on the great house, the cupola and clock tower of *Thoresby Hall*. The seat of the Pierrepont family is the only one of the Dukeries still privately lived in: Clumber is pulled down, Rufford a ruin, Welbeck a college, Worksop but a small house attached to the stableyard of a vanished palace, Thoresby, the last to be built (or rebuilt), alone survives. We approach the house and cross the bridge: the great mass of Salvin's palace stands before us. It is the third house to occupy the site: the a *tour de force*. The visitor enters the porch: the low entrance hall leads to a staircase, and so up to the *Great Hall*. This is dramatic: a series of arches below, galleries above, the grand staircase disappearing through a central arch, a mammoth fireplace, a hammerbeam roof, portraits in baroque frames, armour suspended upon the walls; the antiquity, the importance of the Pierreponts, the solemnity of their house—all this is achieved in Salvin's Thoresby. The family had lost their dukedom: this colossal house went some way to make up for their now being mere earls. The *State Rooms* open up along the S front: Drawing Room, Library, Morning Room, Dining Room; in the Library is a festive chimney-piece portraying in carved oak the Major Oak and the figures of Robin Hood and Little John; after all, we are in the heart of Sherwood Forest. The Park is vast. As at Clumber, it contains its own private village, *Perlethorpe*, with its own church by Salvin (1876), but emphatically a village church, rather than a private chapel. Near by, the Kennels alone survive of Carr's Thoresby—a beautiful Palladian arch (now filled in) on the axis of the E front of the 18th-century house. Now forgotten, it is one of the great attractions of Thoresby. The last Earl Manvers died in 1955, and Thoresby will once again pass through the female line; meantime it is still the home of the family. It is open to the public in the summer; however it must be mentioned that the whole house is threatened continually by subsidence from the local colliery. Ominous cracks appear everywhere: the survival of this great house is imperative.

Thorney [9] A remote outpost of Notts, almost in Lincs: the frontier here twists and turns, and reaches out to embrace Thorney, deeply embowered in woods. It is well worth exploring. *Thorney Hall*, a handsome three-storeyed brick,

Georgian house, home of the Neviles, was sold and pulled down in the early 1960s, but the *Church* which they built in 1849 is as magnificent as it is unexpected. Designed by L.N. Cottingham in the Norman style, it is for a small village enormous: it is also of exceptional quality. The carving of the W doorway, intricately undercut, the details of the frieze, the great dragons' heads protruding from the four corners, the bellcote at the W end, the highly ornamental casket-like turret at the junction of nave and chancel—all this is remarkable. Within, the same grand scale: a great aisleless nave, a raised chancel, pulpit and lectern both in stone, large Victorian font—the original Norman font slumps in the corner (the Victorians, after all, could do better), magnifical furniture in the sanctuary. It is sad that so ancient a family as the Neviles, who first came here in the 16th century (descended from a younger son of Raby) is commemorated by no monument, except the modest tablet to the last owner who died after the Second World War; there are two hatchments (19th century); older monuments must have been destroyed with the old church, of which two arches have been rebuilt in the churchyard. The service wing and stable buildings of the Hall survive: on the site of the house itself a modest suburban residence has been built. Since the break-up of the estate many new bungalows have been built in the village.

Thoroton [11] (the first syllable is pronounced as in 'thorough') The spire is prominent in the view from Flawborough: this is quiet Vale of Belvoir country, gently undulating, much cultivated; there are wide views everywhere, and the Castle, prominent on its hill, seems never far away. The *spire* is the thing: there is a row of gargoyles, beasts and comic heads below the quatre-foil parapet, but the chief glory is the richly canopied ogival niche on

the W front; the pedestal is empty—the Reformers saw to that—but angels and attendant figures still stand (or float) on either side of the elaborately carved and crocketed canopy under which the figure of the patron saint stood. The church was much restored by Hakewill in 1869, and the chancel rebuilt: homely medieval interior with EE arcades. The village is rich in good brick cottages and houses; there is a winsome 'double pile' house in the main street, with sash windows and farm buildings. Near by, in a farmyard, is a medieval stone dovecote, sprucely thatched. The distinguished and ancient family of Thoroton take their name from here: Dr Robert Thoroton was the great 17th-century antiquary and historian of the county (*see* Car Colston and Flintham).

Thorpe [12] Speeding down the Foss Way one catches a glimpse of a small village away to the E: a humble little church, a good-looking late Georgian house next door, a handful of cottages and farm buildings; approaching Thorpe from Hawton one gets the same impression, but the scene is dominated by the *Manor Farm* standing on rising ground ahead, an 18th-century brick house with high garden walls, a house incorporating fragments of the mansion of the Molyneux family, a branch of the Molyneux of Hawton; the pond below the terrace is perhaps a relic of an elaborate garden. The little church was largely rebuilt in 1873; the tower is old, and there is a 14th-century effigy inside (the wife of Sir William de Thorpe), and an ancient font; on the E wall outside are the initials of the rector at the time of the restoration: 'E.W. 1873'. It is the grandson of the Revd Edward Wood who now lives at the Old Rectory next door, a charming early 19th-century house with sash windows and wide overhanging eaves. The Roman town of Ad Pontem lay on the Foss a short distance to the W,

Thurgarton Priory

guarding the bridge that crossed the Trent just beyond.

Thrumpton [13] Off the main road (A453) a quiet lane leads to a secluded dead-end village and a great house: the street, with 18th- and early 19th-century estate cottages, leads past the church to an embattled, turreted gatehouse, and so to the house. *Thrumpton Hall* was built by Gervase Pigot I in the early 17th century, and altered and glorified by his son, Gervase Pigot II, after the Restoration. It is an H-shaped house of brick with stone dressings, with Flemish gables to the wings, and a loggia between them on both fronts. The entrance on the N side leads into a panelled *Great Hall* with screens at either end: to dine in this room is like dining in hall in one of the smaller colleges at Oxford or Cambridge. At the W end the screens entrance leads to the staircase, a staircase of great magnificence, with balustrades of carved acanthus scrolls, newel posts with vases, and dado rails of equally carved splendour. Doorcases at the foot of the stairs, and on the landing, are also elaborately carved. Downstairs, the *Oak Room* contains delightful panelling and carving of Charles II's time; and the Library, occupying the centre of the S front, was handsomely redecorated in the early 19th century. Above this, on the first floor, is the great room of the house, *The Saloon*, decorated sumptuously by Gervase Pigot II, and containing a late 18th-century marble chimneypiece. At the end of the 17th century Thrumpton was bought by John Emerton of the Middle Temple, who bequeathed it to his nephew, John Wescomb Emerton, who succeeded in 1745 and reigned till 1823. It subsequently passed (in the female line) to the 8th Lord Byron; after the death of the 10th baron, who was squarson of the parish, it was acquired by his nephew, Mr George Seymour, who has done a great deal to restore and redecorate it and who opens it to the public during the summer. The *park* is also a delight: on the N side it is watered by a lake, formed from a quiet backwater of the Trent: on the S and W side the ground rises steeply, and from the summit there is an unexpected view down to the railway line far below, with its castellated portal to the Redhill tunnel, and across to the River Soar which joins the Trent near by. The *Church* has a 13th-century tower; the chancel was rebuilt by Street in 1871, and the alabaster reredos, the pulpit and the font are his work. There is a grand monument to the first Gervase Pigot (Mr Arthur Oswald has suggested that it may be by Sir William Wilson) with attendant angels holding back curtains beneath an elaborate canopy; this, and later monuments to the Emertons, banished to the tower in the Victorian restoration, have been very properly re-erected in the church by the present squire.

Thurgarton [11] The priory of Austin Canons here was founded in 1187 by Ralph d'Eyncourt: the beautiful, mutilated, fragment of their *Church* is still the parish church, and stands against the 18th-century house—called *Thurgarton Priory*—which faces W across an undulating park; the village, on the main Nottingham–Southwell road (A612), with the *Red Lion* and a pleasant handful of old houses and cottages, is set in a tumble of low hills on the W side of the Trent Valley. The lane to the church passes the high wall of the kitchen garden of the great house: there was originally a W front with two towers; the NW tower survives, but the red-brick Georgian house encroaches on the S side of the church, and the SW tower has gone. Even now, with the imposing EE W doorway and the surviving tower (both of considerable beauty), the remaining four bays of the nave with its 13th-century arcades and harmonious Victorian chancel (by T.C. Hine, (1852)), the church cannot fail to impress; there are 15th-century misericords, 18th-century monuments to the Cooper family, and many windows filled with colourful Victorian glass. At the Dissolution the Priory was granted to William Cooper, cup-bearer to Henry VIII: John Gilbert Cooper built the present house in 1777 on the site of the monastic buildings. He was a scholar and minor poet and receives an occasional mention in Boswell; in one longish poem he is enraptured by the delights of life at Thurgarton, and speaks of Horace and Catullus drinking Falernian wine after rambling in his groves. Two or three families succeeded the Coopers here; in 1884 the first Bishop of Southwell (Dr Ridding) came to live here; it is now owned by Boot's, who use it as the headquarters of a research department.

Tithby [14] (or Tythby) A small village in delightful position on the rising ground S of Bingham: the endearing, entertaining little *Church* stands in a churchyard above the street and is part medieval, part Georgian; the base of the tower is medieval and stone, the upper part Georgian and brick; a large weather-vane crowns its pyramid top. There is a Georgian porch— and inside the same dichotomy: a 14th-century S arcade, but with a big Georgian window in the aisle; an early 19th-century Gothic N arcade, where Victorian furnishings prevail, but otherwise 18th-century box pews and two-decker pulpit. Mr Train has explained this odd assortment: the S side of the church was the responsibility of Cropwell Butler (where there was no church), the N belonged to Tithby. Thus they asserted their independence. A W gallery, a Royal Arms of George III; and Creed, Lord's Prayer, and Commandment Boards adorning the sanctuary. The Tithby Dairy makes very good cream cheese.

Tollerton [14] A splendid afternoon's entertainment. *The lodge* at the entrance to the park sets the tone; a jaunty arch with absurdly tall pepper-pot finials, and a lodge squeezed in at the junction of the lanes, all in stuccoed brick—the stucco somewhat peeling; the lane leads on towards the church: there is a pair of 'folly' cottages of amusing design, a very tall, late 17th- or early 18th-century farmhouse, the background of trees in the park, and we are at the church. The approach is by a footpath bordering the garden of the Old Rectory (18th century and earlier). And what a *Church* it is! It is the oddest building: the tower is stone, the body of the building stucco, the clerestory brick—all in a homely early 19th-century Gothick style. The interior is charming and eccentric: the arcades are ancient (though somewhat touched up); the nave has a flat roof; there is a squire's pew in the W gallery (with marble fireplace); the chancel is low, and has a Norman pillar piscina. At the E end of the S aisle is the Pendock Barry mausoleum: a wrought-iron screen of elaborate design leads into a top-lit chamber, built in 1812 in memory of Pendock Barry's wife; a great memorial fills the E wall, smaller obelisk memorials occupy niches to left and right; plaster figures of apostles look down from above, everywhere are shields of arms with supporters, crests and banners. The Barrys held Tollerton from the 13th century to the 16th, when their heiress married a Pendock; at the end of the 17th the Pendock heiress married a Neale, but in 1812 Pendock Neale changed his name to Barry; his son, Pendock Barry Neale became Pendock Barry Barry and died, a bachelor, in 1847, the last of the line. Father and son had antiquarian interests: both were Magdalen men and fancied that the new tower they built for the church resembled Magdalen Tower. Seven hatchments of their family adorn the church; the eighth is of Mrs Susannah Davies, who bought the property afterwards; the E window is in her memory (1874). Across the churchyard wall there is a good view of the Hall— renamed *Roclaveston Manor* by Pendock Barry (Tollerton being a corruption of Roclaveston). Originally a 17th-century house, it was in turn Palladianized in the 18th century, and then Gothickized. Its façade is stuccoed—with battlements, pinnacles and turrets; a side wing ends in a clock tower, and the open arcade connecting house and church was originally a cloister linking the two. After being used for a time as a Congregational College, it is now St Hugh's College, the junior seminary for the Roman Catholic Diocese of Nottingham.

Treswell [6] At the junction of minor roads in the remote country between Retford and the Trent: cottages, a Victorian terrace or two, petrol pumps. The *church* stands in tree-embowered isolation, the Lee Beck watering its pretty churchyard, a spacious Victorian Gothic rectory behind. The approach is from the E: Dec chancel, embattled Perp nave and tower, make an attractive composition. Inside, a Perp arcade and the Dec traceried windows with their clear glass are a pleasure.

Trowell [13] A familiar name once, when Trowell was chosen as the *Festival of Britain village* in 1951. Photographs appeared everywhere of the decided square medieval tower, with a backdrop of industrial

Tuxford

chimneys and steelworks. Heaven knows why Trowell was chosen; however, it was a pleasant change from the overworked villages of Sussex or the Cotswolds. Now, in addition to the Erewash, two railway lines, and two main roads which cut off the church from whatever is left of the village, there is the new M1 to the E. So poor Trowell is completely encircled, strangled. Moreover, there is also on the E the overgrown Nottingham Canal, winding its way N towards Cossall. Of the church, the chancel is 13th century and the conspicuous tower Perp. There is an attractive 17th- or early 18th-century farmhouse near the church; Trowell Hall, the other side of the M1, is Victorian; and the village pub commemorates the Festival of Britain.

Tuxford [8] The main road (A6075) climbs the hill—to the long white front of the *Newcastle Arms*. Tuxford is a charming little

decayed market town (its charter granted in 1218); it became prosperous in coaching days, with the Great North Road and the road from Lincoln to Ollerton meeting at the top of the hill: now the A1 romps past at the bottom of the hill, by-passing the town and crossing the A6075 by a bridge. *Tuxford Hall* is a tall, brick 18th-century house, with a plain front facing the street—but with two wings ending in great castellated bows with Gothick windows at the back, clearly visible from the by-pass. Opposite, the late *17th-century school* is an equal pleasure: founded in 1669, built of brick, with hipped roof and sash windows, rusticated pilasters with balls at the top on either side of the front door and an inscription above, it is an interesting and unusual building. Charles Read who founded it also founded the school at Corby in Lincolnshire—another beautiful little building, now the Willoughby Memorial Gallery. His school here is now the Public

Library. A little higher up the hill, the *Church* stands above the street; the exterior is predominantly Perp, with a Dec tower and spire. Inside, there are earlier arcades in the nave, a somewhat restored Perp screen, a crude stone carving at the E end of the S aisle depicting the martyrdom of St Lawrence—with a late 15th-century figure of the saint in the window above—and a 17th-century font. This has a cover dated 1673, with, above it, a magnificent hanging canopy suspended from the roof. On the N side of the chancel, guarded by an iron screen, is the 18th-century mortuary chapel of the White family, baronets, of Wallingwells and formerly of Tuxford (*see* Carlton-in-Lindrick), containing the imposing tomb of Sir John White (1625) with recumbent effigies (his wife was a Harpur of Swarkstone, Derbyshire, his mother a sister of the great Lord Burghley); an unusual tablet to Charles Lawrence (brother of the 1st Bt), captain in the Foot Guards,

Upton Hall

killed at Bayonne in 1814; and two big hatchments, one with no less than 28 quarterings. The road N from the Market Place is the Old North Road; from the top of the hill there are wide views—to the E to the three enormous power stations along the Trent, and East Markham Church: to the W to West Markham Church in the valley below. In Newcastle Street (to the W) is a little brick lock-up, dated 1823 in bold letters; the lane leads on to Egmanton and Laxton.

Underwood [10] The spire of the church is a conspicuous landmark, here in the scarred countryside close to the Erewash Valley, close to the Derbyshire border. It is colliery country. Much housing along the main road—with the imposing

Church the only building of note, designed by the Birmingham architect, J.A. Chatwin, for Earl Cowper, of Beauvale (1890). The spire has an open belfry and a prominent clock.

Upper Broughton, *see* Broughton, Upper

Upton [11] The road from Newark to Southwell: expectancy is in the air. Wide views to the S towards the Trent and the low Trent Hills; a backcloth of green undulating country to the N. The road makes its way between farmhouses and cottages, gardens and orchards, turns to pass the Hall and its policies, turns again by the *Cross Keys*, and carries on. North End House, the Old Vicarage, the thatched Post

Office, the Manor, the Grange with its imposing porch, Pepper's Cottage—this is the perfect Notts village of warm red brick and warm red pantiles. *The Hall* is as unexpected as it is delightful, a spacious and elegant Grecian villa with central dome and impressive Ionic portico, stuccoed and washed pale apricot: it might be standing in a large garden in Brighton. It was built *c.*1830 by W.J. Donthorne for Thomas Wright, banker of Nottingham, and is now the headquarters of the Royal Horological Society. *The tower of the church* with its nine pinnacles—a tall central pinnacle presiding over all—is a landmark: inside, an EE arcade, a 14th-century chantry chapel with a lengthy squint to the high altar, and gargantuan ancient chest; the first

From the roof of **Welbeck**

floor room in the tower was a chamber for the chantry priest, an upper room a dovecote. And at the W end of the village is the first glimpse of the tower and spires of Southwell.

Walesby [8] An overgrown village—a kind of 'overspill' for New Ollerton—with endless rows of semis by the main road; but there is a nucleus of older village near the *Church*. Ancient beech trees adorn the churchyard: the Perp W tower bears the arms of the Stanhopes of Haughton, and the aisleless N façade with its rhythm of Perp windows in clerestory and below is probably part of their rebuilding.

The S arcade is 13th century, the chancel 14th; there are a few 16th-century pews, a 17th-century pulpit, and the medieval effigy of a lady from the ruined chapel at Haughton (q.v.). A beautifully furnished, devotional church.

Walkeringham [5] Between the Trent and the Chesterfield Canal. The Manor House is an attractive fragment of Elizabethan brickwork, once the home of a branch of the Williamsons of East Markham. The *Church* 'a large ancient pile' (White's *Notts Directory*, 1853), has an embattled Perp exterior with

bold W tower, and much old woodwork in the wide, spacious interior—benches, pulpit, screen (the upper part oddly removed to form vestry screen), and much attractive Victorian glass, by Wailes and others. The important tomb to Francis Williamson (1639) by Edward Marshall is in poor state of repair; Marshall, distinguished sculptor of London, built the great portico at the Vyne (Hampshire) in 1656, and his work here deserves careful restoration.

Warsop [8] Mining country: Church Warsop with its dignified *Church* and a scattering of old stone

The Riding School yard, **Welbeck**

buildings stands on its hill to the N, commanding a wide view of the collieries around Mansfield and along the Derbyshire borderland, and of the town of Market Warsop at its feet, separated by the River Meden and green commonlands. There is little to see in Market Warsop but dingy streets: Church Warsop is well worth a visit. The *Church* is distinguished, with its heavily buttressed tower (Norman, with a later 14th-century pinnacled top), its spacious nave and chancel. The S arcade is EE at its most elegant, the N Dec; the clerestory and low embattled SE chantry (now vestry) added to the chancel are Perp. There are several monuments, of which the best is to John Rolleston (d.1651); the most interesting is

Welbeck; Details of the chapel
altar front by Henry Wilson
and of the Gothick Hall

that to Henry Gally Knight (1786–
1846) 'the dutiful son of a
widowed mother . . . a poet . . . a
traveller . . . a man of kindness and
benefactor of his church . . .' He was
MP for the county, and will be for
ever blessed as the donor to Southwell Minster of the glass in the E
windows from the Temple Church
in Paris. The E window commemorates Sir Richard FitzHerbert of Tissington: 'To the glory of
God, and in memory of a good man,
Sir Richard FitzHerbert, Bt. Rector of Warsop, 1872–1896, Lord of
the Manor 1896–1906.' To the W
of the church stands the *Old Hall*
with its attendant buildings: the
17th-century barn has been converted into a parish hall; the house
itself has a number of medieval and
16th-century features, and forms
with the barn and other old farm
buildings a group of considerable
charm.

Welbeck [8] 'The borders of Nottinghamshire and Derbyshire' writes Mark Bence-Jones (in *The Cavaliers*, Constable, 1976) 'are to this day dominated by the personality of William Cavendish, the Cavalier Duke of Newcastle. His castle at Bolsover still rises from its cliff in that strange, broken country bordered by the moors and high hills, just as it does in the plates of his book on horsemanship, where its turrets and cupolas form the background to illustrations of himself performing *caprioles* and *belottades* on his noble Spanish mares. Below the castle, his riding house remains as a monument to his passion for the *haute école*, as does his other riding house at Welbeck a few miles to the east in Sherwood Forest ...' The great domain of Welbeck extends to the gates of Worksop on the N, and abuts the Derbyshire frontier on the W. It is still the property of the Cavendish–Bentinck family, and is not open to the public. Part of *Welbeck Abbey* is used as an army college: the state rooms are reserved for family use. Welbeck was founded as a Premonstratensian house in 1153; after the Dissolution it passed through various hands until in 1597 Sir Charles Cavendish (third son of Bess of Hardwick) leased it from his brother-in-law Gilbert Talbot, and bought it 10 years later. The families of all the great houses of the Dukeries were related to each other, and all were descended from Bess; indeed, for a generation Welbeck, Clumber and Haughton all belonged to one man, John Holles, Duke of Newcastle. But that is to anticipate. Welbeck has passed through the female line three times. William Cavendish, 1st Duke of Newcastle, Royalist Commander, skilled horseman, devoted servant of Charles I—always known as 'the loyal duke'—was son of Sir Charles; his son, the 2nd Duke, had only a daughter, who married her cousin John Holles, Earl of Clare, of Clumber and Haughton, who was created Duke of Newcastle (of the second cre-

One of **Welbeck**'s more than fifty lodges

ation). Once again there was only a daughter: Lady Henrietta Cavendish-Holles, who inherited Welbeck and married Edward Harley, 2nd Earl of Oxford, while her first cousin, Thomas Pelham-Holles, inherited Clumber and Haughton. But once more there was no son, and so a daughter, Lady Margaret Cavendish-Harley, inherited Welbeck. She married William Bentinck, 2nd Duke of Portland; the succession has been direct since then. The 3rd Duke was twice Prime Minister to George III, the 5th a legendary eccentric. The building history of Welbeck has been equally chequered: Robert Smythson made plans for a grand

new house for Sir Charles, but only one wing of this was built. John Smythson built a great riding school for the 'loyal' duke in 1623, and another wing over the monastic undercroft. In the early 18th century Vanbrugh and Talman were called in by John Holles to plan a palatial house, but nothing was done. His daughter, Lady Oxford, remodelled the Robert Smythson wing, now known as the Oxford Wing, and the great hall. Later in the century Carr of York Georgianized the gabled W front for the 3rd Duke, in an attractive castellated style, and formed the state rooms in the E front which, however, still remained gabled and

Manor house, **North Wheatley**

great hall: with its plaster fan vault and Gothick adornments, it was admired by Horace Walpole. Along the E front are Carr's *State Rooms*: Swan Drawing Room, Red Drawing Room, Library, Ante Room—all handsomely decorated: round the corner the rooms are those rebuilt by Sir Ernest George after the fire; at the N end there is a grand Edwardian Dining Room (now used as the Masters' Common Room). The *Smythson Riding School* now forms a vast North Wing; half of it is the library, half the chapel (both used by the College), designed by J.D. Sedding and Henry Wilson, whose brilliant and beautiful furnishings and decorations in the chapel are specially notable: altar, font, choir stalls, lectern, bronze gates are all masterpieces. Parallel with the Smythson building is an 18th-century office block almost matching Smythson's work: together they form a delightful *rectangular courtyard*, with gilded weather-vanes crowning the cupolas at either end; indeed they constitute the least altered part of Welbeck. The 5th Duke's building activities and achievements are in a class of their own: below ground, and adjoining the Smythson Riding School, he built a vast *Ballroom*, the largest room in Europe without supporting pillars; adjoining it he built a suite of library rooms (or supper rooms)—now used as classrooms by the college—approached by a top-lit conservatory; on the other side of the ballroom another top-lit conservatory was to lead to another vast room, a bachelors' hall, on which work had begun at the time of his death. Passages underground were fitted with tramlines, so that food could be carried in trucks from the kitchen to wherever was necessary. One of these passages leads to the medieval undercroft, where a 12th-century door opens into a wine cellar. Outside the house he built long underground tunnels: one led to Worksop, another to the new Riding School and Stables which he built

informal on that side. The most extraordinary, and indeed the biggest, building episode was that undertaken by the eccentric 5th Duke—but all his additions were underground. After his death (1879) there was much tidying up to do: the house was barely habitable, and the garden full of builders' rubble. A great Library and Chapel were formed in the Smythson Riding School (which was joined to the house by a great curving wing) and in 1902, after a fire, Sir Ernest George rebuilt the Oxford wing and

remodelled the exterior of the whole house. The refacing of the E front in formal classical style, with its rusticated, pedimented centrepiece, is his work. The approach to the house is from the W, up the *Mall*; the *Oxford Wing* is on the right and, although Georgianized, the little cupola is a clue to its early 17th-century origins; Sir Ernest George's pedimented frontispiece ahead, with its *porte-cochère*, greets the arriving guest. The finest room here is the *Gothick Hall*, a remodelling by Lady Oxford of the 17th-century it acts as a kind of pre-Sandhurst sixth form college, and the whole place is splendidly maintained.

Wellow [8] Undulating country: a village with a green, on which stands a tall, gaily painted maypole. Red-brick cottages around, a Primitive Methodist chapel of 1827, *Rock House* with its plastered, overhanging timber front, a public house or two, and behind the *Red Lion*, the church. A SW tower, 14th-century nave and wide S aisle, all much restored by Ewan Christian, who also rebuilt the chancel in 1879; a dark over-scraped interior with Victorian fittings, another Foljambe memorial window in S aisle (*see* Ollerton), and Norman font. Wellow Hall, with its plain 18th-century front and sash windows, stands above the street; Wellow House opposite is Victorian, now a prep school. The road turns suddenly and —great shock—Ollerton Colliery with its chimneys and winding towers and blackened face is round the corner.

West Bridgford, *see* Nottingham

West Drayton, *see* Drayton, West

West Leake, *see* Leake, West

West Markham, *see* Markham, West

Weston [9] Sometimes called Weston-on-Trent, which it isn't: the Trent is a considerable distance away to the E. The village stands in the low undulating country between the A1 and the main railway line, and is a prominent landmark from both. The church is all battlemented and pinnacled, with a Perp tower and spire, unpinnacled and uncrocketed in characteristic Notts style; in fact the Perp clerestory crowns a 13th-century nave; well furnished interior with orderly, early 19th-century pews. Landscape of pylons, marching relentlessly across the flatlands from High Marnham power station.

Widmerpool

in the park; indeed he built vast ranges of new buildings here, and all around the estate identical Tudor-style lodges: wherever they appear they herald Welbeck property—there are 40 or 50 of them. Yet this lonely, legendary, eccentric man camped out in a few rooms in the main house: few saw him, still fewer knew him. A vivid account of the house after his death is given by Lady Ottoline Morrell in her *Memoirs* (ed. Robert Gathorne-Hardy, Faber & Faber, 1963). She was half-sister of the 6th Duke, and describes the melancholy state of the place when they visited it for the first time in 1880. The setting of the house is superb: the River Poulter, approaching from the W, feeds a great lake of prodigious length before pursuing its way to render a similar service at Clumber. In 1932 the 7th Duke built a smaller house in the park, which has since been the family home. Soon after the Second World War the army college was established in the major portion of the house: known as *Welbeck College*

Willoughby-on-the-Wolds

West Stockwith, *see* Stockwith, West

Whatton(-in-the-Vale) [14] The A52 carries all the traffic to Nottingham or Grantham: the village, happily by-passed, is secluded and shady with its labyrinth of lanes, its houses and gardens behind high walls. Many good cottages and houses were built by Thomas Dickinson Hall, Victorian squire, who built Whatton Manor in Elizabethan style (1840)—now recently replaced by a smaller house

in the Georgian manner. Spacious and splendid *Church*, with central tower and low spire: T.D. Hall has been much criticized for his restoration and rebuilding—indeed he rebuilt the long chancel and (with the assistance of Thomas Butler of Langar, q.v.) the tower and spire. Be that as it may, it is all gracious and full of interest: the base of the tower is Norman, the nave Dec; in the N aisle are two carved corbels, with canopies above, of exceptional beauty: one of King David playing his harp, the other of an angel music-

ian (14th century); there is a 14th-century effigy of a priest, and two other 14th-century tombs (Hugh de Newmarch and Sir Richard de Watton); the font is dated 1662; and there is much good Victorian glass, notably the E window in the S aisle, by Burne-Jones and Morris and Co. Of special interest is the incised slab to Thomas Cranmer (1502), father of the archbishop, at the E end of the N aisle. In 1957 this chapel was refurnished in memory of his eminent son: the furnishings and ornaments are handsome, and a tablet pays tribute to the man to whom is due the glorious language of the Book of Common Prayer—now, alas, so widely abandoned for the commonplace jargon of the Alternative Service Book.

Wheatley, North and South [5] In the pretty country of the Wheatley Hills, between Retford and the Trent; lanes dip down into North Wheatley from the main road. The *Church* is one of those aisleless 'hall' churches of the Perp period—like Bole or Lambley—with large windows of clear glass; inside, Norman font, 14th-century pews, 17th-century pulpit. The brass to Edmund Sheffield, citizen vintner of London (1445) has palimpsest inscription 'Joan the wife of Hugo Cokesey' on the reverse. The ancient timber tower staircase is an amusing object. Hard upon the street, at the bottom of the hill, is the 17th-century brick *manor house*, with all kinds of homely classical features in moulded brick—obelisks, Ionic pilasters and lunettes; it is dated 1673. South Wheatley is more or less contiguous: the church was shamelessly pulled down a century ago; only the tower and small Norman chancel arch survive. The vandals were with us then, as now. There are delightful views of old red-brick farm buildings and dovecotes across the valley between the two villages.

Widmerpool [14] Memorable for the sonorous syllables of its name: no doubt Mr Widmerpool of Anthony Powell's novels sprang from a long line of ancestors who took their name from here. But the appearance of the place today is due to another family, the Robertsons or Robinsons (they varied the spelling of their name), mill-owners of Nottingham, Bulwell and Linby: the tall tower of the Victorian hall (built for Major George Robertson by Henry Clutton in 1872) rises among the evergreen plantations of the park; and, half-concealed by cedar trees, their sumptuously

rebuilt *Church* stands up a long drive just below. Its architect seems unrecorded: the tower is in origin 14th century, but the rest was rebuilt between 1888 and 1895. The chancel is vaulted and lavishly adorned with marble shafts to the clustered columns; at the W end is the family mausoleum where the figure of Mrs Robertson (d.1891) reclines on an elaborate marble couch. The Hall is now an AA Patrol Service HQ; a number of expensive modern villas have been built in the grounds, but there is a delectable *cottage ornée* surviving near the church.

Wilford, *see* Nottingham

Willoughby-on-the-Wolds [14] Undulating countryside close to the Leicestershire frontier: the *Church* stands on the edge of the village, overlooking the site of the Battle of Willoughby Field (1648), its chimes gaily heralding the passing quarters. An early 14th-century broach spire, a wide 13th-century nave, a long 14th-century chancel, Georgianized in the 18th century—but medievalized again by W.S. Weatherley in 1891: it is an impressive church. But its great glory is the notable succession of Willoughby tombs, of stone or alabaster, in the N chapel. The great Notts family of Willoughby take their name from this place: descended from Ralph Bugge (pronounced Bouge—hence the three water bougets in their coat of arms), a wealthy wool merchant of Nottingham, who in the 13th century began buying land here, they became in course of time 'de Willoughby'. In the 14th century the family was linked by marriage to the heiress of Wollaton (Nottingham, q.v.), which later became their principal seat, in the 15th to the heiress of Middleton (near Tamworth), from which they later took their title, in the 18th to the heiress of Birdsall, where Lord Middleton lives today. But here in Willoughby lie their earliest ancestors. Against the W wall are the earliest tombs

(c.1300), their identities lost; against the N wall is Sir Richard, Lord Chief Justice in 1333 (ob.1362), with beautifully carved face and robes; his son, also Sir Richard (ob.c.1400) occupies the tomb under the arcade dividing aisle from chapel; the most spectacular of all is that of Sir Hugh (ob.1448), great grandson of the Judge, who with his wife holds place of honour in the centre of the chapel: playful puppies support her feet, a friendly lion his; below, carved panels of the Trinity and of the Virgin, which miraculously survived the Reformation, adorn the two ends of the tomb. On the floor near by an oval brass commemorates Colonel Michael Stanhope (of Shelford, q.v.) 'who was slayne in Willoughby Field in the month of July 1648 in the 24 yeare of his age being a souldier for King Charles the First'.

Winkburn [11] For atmosphere and charm: a quiet lane leads off the main road, fine trees herald the presence of a *gentleman's seat*, and there is a scattering of cottages: no more. But through the lodge gate there is a glimpse of the *Hall*, a decided, square, red-brick house of late 17th- or early 18th-century date, three storeys high, with sash windows. Next to it stands the church (of St John of Jerusalem): visitors to the church are welcome, but are asked to keep to the path which runs along the side of the copse. The tower was rebuilt in 1623, using old materials and some Norman features; the *churchyard* is extremely pretty with many old headstones. There is a Norman S door; inside, the *Church* is a perfect, undisturbed Georgian interior, with box pews, a Jacobean pulpit (with later sounding board), and a rare 17th-century arched screen with plaster tympanum above, bearing the Royal Arms of George III (1764)—reminiscent of Warminghurst in Sussex. The manor of Winkburn, which had belonged to the Knights of St John

Winkburn

of Jerusalem, was granted to William Burnell (auditor to Henry VIII) in 1548; there is an array of monuments to the family from William Burnell (d.1570) to Laurence Barrington Assheton Craven-Smith-Milnes (d.1933). Winkburn then was sold, and the family moved to *Hockerton Manor* near by: in the course of the next 45 years the house became a prep school, a hostel for the workmen building the Staythorpe power station, for a short time a private residence, and for a long time stood empty. It has recently been bought back by Mr Richard Craven-Smith-Milnes (whose father was obliged to sell it), who with his wife has restored and revived it. Old pictures show it as a house with hipped roof, top balustrade and cupola: the present top storey was added in 1805, so tactfully that it is difficult to detect this alteration; indeed with this addition the house is reminiscent of Wren's façades at Hampton Court. Inside, there are handsome 18th-century chimneypieces, and several of the doors have architraves delicately carved with landscape scenes. There is earlier panelling, too, and some very good plaster-work. The terrace commands the view of pastoral countryside: through the wood on the horizon a ride carries the eye obliquely to the distance. From the Hall gate the quiet lane leads on to Maplebeck, across the little River Wink.

Winthorpe [12] There is a grand-stand view, as it were, from the Newark by-pass: the red-brick Victorian church with its tall broach spire, looking like a church in East-bourne or Maidenhead; the Grove, a Palladian, stuccoed villa; Low Wood, an 18th-century house of mellow brick; great walled gardens; and the Hall, prominent in its position overlooking the river and the meadows. But Winthorpe itself is a secluded village, approachable only from behind, from the Gainsborough road, the new by-pass like a long fortifying wall protecting it from the outside world. There are many pleasing 18th- or 19th-century houses and cottages; a few modern 'suburbans' have crept in. *The Hall*, an imposing stone Palladian house, begun for Dr Robert Taylor (Physician to George II), was completed by Roger Pocklington, banker of New-ark, after Taylor's death (1762). Stone steps lead up to the front door on the *piano nobile*; inside, there are handsome rooms adorned with contemporary plasterwork and chimneypieces; the house has recently been rescued from near-dereliction. Mr Pocklington built several charming houses (and fol-lies) in the village, some of which survive; a print, published in 1807, shows little vignettes of these: *the Grove* (built for his son, c.1800) is elegant with its flight of steps up to the front door, with its sashes and lunettes: *Low Wood* is dated 1787, and an inscription over the front door records that 'The first stone of this house was laid by Roger Pock-lington junior, and his sister Elizabeth, June 25th 1787, aged 11 years, aged 10 years.' Dial House,

the Academy, Old Rectory Farm (and a cottage *ornée* opposite), Win-thorpe House, the Cottage, and the *Lord Nelson* provide further pleasures. The church, built for the Revd William Handley in 1886 by S. Gambier Parry, is dignified and attractive, even if unexpected and somewhat incongruous: a well-furnished interior, with a few minor monuments from the previous 18th-century church.

Wiseton [5] The Roman road from Clayworth travels NE and soon reaches the plantations of *Wiseton*. The house is embowered in rhododendrons: a lime avenue, aligned on the entrance, makes for the high ground to the N; there is a great Victorian stable quad-rangle, a cottage or two, and that is all, except for the Chesterfield Canal, which here makes a wide loop, and then turns towards Drakeholes. The Ackloms came to Wiseton in the 17th century: their most interesting member was that 'improving' squire, Jonathan Acklom—'Mr Acklom' as he al-ways seems to be called. An engrav-ing of 1792 shows the house as it was: a tall, early 18th-century building with bow-fronted pavilion wings, each crowned with a little cupola. A garden temple stands on a little tumulus, overlooking the canal, and a barge passes by. The house has gone: it was pulled down in 1960 and replaced by a smaller 'Georgian' house. The Ackloms have gone: their heiress married the 3rd Earl Spencer (1814); later it passed to the Laycocks, of whom the last was General Laycock, Gov-ernor of Malta. But the setting remains delightful: Mr Acklom's avenues are still in their glory, his Palladian landmarks, with which he set out to improve the surround-ing 'eminences'—the *White Swan* at Drakeholes, the farmhouse at Pusto Hill, another at Blaco Hill—are clearly visible on the hilltops, all scholarly Palladian buildings. To add to the pleasures, at Drakeholes the Chesterfield Canal goes under-

ground for a considerable distance on its way to join the Trent at Stockwith. Two dilapidated little lodges to a vanished entrance to Wiseton stand near by, charming but melancholy.

Wollaton, *see* Nottingham

Woodborough [11] A long village street of warm red brick—cottages, splendid farm buildings, one or two larger houses: the *Hall Farmhouse* (No. 5) with two tall gables is inscribed 'Philip Lacock Esquire, 1710'; and *Woodborough Hall* op-posite, surrounded by shrubberies and almost invisible, is a late 17th-century house, also built by Philip Lacock, and containing a hand-some scrolled staircase. Externally the house was Victorianized by that interesting eccentric, Mansfield Parkyns, descendant of the wres-tling baronet of Bunny (q.v.), who after spending years in Abyssinia (he was the author of *Life in Abys-sinia*), returned to Notts and came to live here. He carved the choir stalls, pulpit and tower screen in the *Church*, and his grave is by the S door. The Dec chancel is of con-siderable splendour, with great curvilinear E window, built by Richard de Strelley: the arms of Strelley of Strelley and Strelley of Woodborough adorn the gable; Perp nave and W tower; (blocked) Norman N doorway and Norman font; fragments of medieval glass in chancel; one window by Morris and Co and E window by Kempe.

Worksop [5] An ancient and historic borough: it is the duty of the Lord of the Manor to provide a glove for the Sovereign at the Coron-ation. But for the casual visitor today it may be hard to appreciate this, approaching the town from the E or W, past the collieries of Manton or Shireoaks, or entering it from the N through endless acres of raw red semis, past factories and in-dustrial estates. The thing to do is to approach Worksop from the S, along the B6005, between the great ducal estates of Welbeck and Clumber. Before descending the hill into the town, Worksop College (looking every inch a Woodard school) appears on the right: the great baroque gates (1894) to Welbeck on the left. Sparken Hill, with its large suburban houses, leads into the town, into Park Street with its Georgian houses, past the little RC church of St Mary, built in 1838 for the 12th Duke of Norfolk by M.E. Hadfield, a little Perp style building with a charming, intimate interior, and a lofty hammerbeam roof. Walk round the *churchyard*, raised above the street, for a good view of the town, and of Worksop Priory to the NE. Park Street leads into the Market Place. This is certainly disappointing: the *Town Hall* (by Charles Gilbert, 1851) faces into Potter Street with its Italianate front, exposing its formless side to the Market Place. The public lavatories seem to be the most prominent building here—though the *Ship Inn* opposite, with its plastered, timber-framed, overhanging front provides some air of charm and antiquity. Potter Street to the E still contains a few 18th-century houses, though many of the best have been successfully destroyed in recent years to make way for a hefty, hideous, extension to the Town Hall. Bridge Street to the N, however, starts well with a number of dignified Georgian houses—such as the *Lion Hotel*—though in many cases anonymous modern shopfronts disfigure their façades. Beyond the bridge over the River Ryton there is little to see, except for a glimpse of the Chesterfield Canal, the 1850 Jacobean Railway Station, and St John's Church with its prominent spire (by R.C. Clarke, 1867)—a large church with a rather bare, scraped interior. *Worksop Priory*, of course, is what everybody comes to see. It may be approached down Potter Street, where the great 14th-century gatehouse faces the street; alternatively the Memorial Avenue leads direct to the W front—a rather meagre piece of 1920s town planning, with war memorial, hospital, and public library lining a kind of 'processional way'; none of these is a building of note. But Worksop Priory is superb. Founded by William de Lovetot *c*.1120, the W front with its twin towers is Norman architecture at its most simple and severe. The pinnacles and battlements are, of course, Perp; otherwise it is only a matter of a few small windows, two grand doorways, and a big Norman window over the great door: all else is bare and unadorned. Inside, the nave is long and imposing; the arcades are Trans, with nailhead decoration on the alternating round and octagonal pillars, a triforium composed of large round arches and narrow pointed ones, with the round arches breaking into the clerestory above, and a clerestory of round-headed windows set above the narrow openings below; it is an unusual composition. At the Dissolution the monastic parts of the church were pulled down, with the exception of the Lady chapel, which, opening out of the S transept, remained detached and roofless until 1922, when Sir Harold Breakspear restored it, rebuilt the S transept (1929) and the N transept (1935) on the model of the old work—a harmonious and sympathetic reconstruction. In the early 1970s a new E end was added, with admirable and remarkable courage, designed by Mr Laurence King: a squat central tower with tapering flèche, and gabled choir. It is sad to have to say that the new work is not worthy of the noble church: it is neither harmonious nor sympathetic; the design seems insensitive, the details crude. The 13th-century *Lady chapel*, with its slender lancet windows, is a building of special beauty, a graceful foil to the more solid splendour of the 12th-century church. *Worksop College* was founded in 1890—the sixth and last school founded by Nathaniel Woodard; indeed it opened in 1895, after the founder's death. Woodard had a keen eye for a good site, and here as at Lancing or Denstone the position on the S side of the town, with wide views over Clumber and Sherwood Forest, is very fine; the land was the gift of the 8th Duke of Newcastle. All the original buildings were designed by R.H. Carpenter (he, or his father R.C. Carpenter, had designed all the schools founded by Woodard); here his brick ranges with their stepped gables have a distinctive Flemish air. The *Dining Hall* with its hammerbeam roof is specially successful; the *Chapel*, needless to say, is the grandest building, the gift, in 1911, of the 14th Viscount Mountgarret, and designed by Sir Aston Webb (after Carpenter's death). It completes the long S range of the college, and with its prominent E turrets and cupolas, and its handsomely furnished interior, is a building of some splendour. On the W side of the town, in Newcastle Avenue, is *St Anne's Church*, an imposing and characteristic work of Paley and Austin (1911), with bold tower and Perp features. To the N of the town, on the A57, is the hamlet of Gateford. *Gateford Hill*, on the high ground behind, is a good-looking neo-classical house of 1824, built for the Machin family by George Crockney. It is now offices. Close to the road is *Gateford Hall*, in origin the medieval manor house, much altered in the 17th century; *Gateford House* near by, is a tall early 18th-century brick house, now the home of the Machins. The lordship of the manor of Worksop descended from the Lovetots to the Furnivals, and so to the Talbots, Earls of Shrewsbury. The 6th Earl, Bess of Hardwick's fourth and last husband, built an incredible house, Worksop Manor, in the late 1570s, designed by Robert Smythson (who built Hardwick for Bess). Immensely tall, and crowned with cupolas and domed lantern towers, it outdid all the other 'progeny houses' of the Elizabethan age. It passed by marriage to the Dukes of

Norfolk, but was burnt down in 1761. Immediately the 9th Duke and his wife (Mary Blount, herself an amateur architect) commissioned James Paine to design a new house which should have been the greatest and grandest private house in England. Pictures exist of the N front, all that was ever completed: an immense façade, 23 bays in extent, with rusticated ground floor and enormous pedimented pilastered centrepiece. The heir, a much loved nephew, died of measles: the Duke and Duchess, prostrated with grief, did no more, and lost all interest. Later dukes became more interested in reviving and restoring Arundel, and in 1839 the 12th Duke sold the estate to the 4th Duke of Newcastle. Having no need for another great house so close to Clumber, Newcastle pulled the mansion down, leaving only the rusticated base and the great stable yard, and converted the service wing and part of the courtyard into a modest residence, which was occupied in the mid-19th century by the 4th Lord Foley. In 1890 the 7th Duke sold the property to Sir John Robinson; it is his family who own the place today. The *Stable Yard*, built by the 8th Duke of Norfolk—which appears in Buck's print of the Elizabethan house—survives: a monumental courtyard, like the court of a Cambridge college. A cupola-crowned archway at one end, the triumphal arch built by James Paine and crowned with the Norfolk lion at the other, lead into what was the *cour d'honneur* in front of the mansion. Here James Paine's ground floor serves now as an immense and impressive garden wall, crowned with the urns which orig-

inally surmounted the façade; this, with Paine's screen of Doric columns and his triumphal arch, are an eloquent reminder of vanished magnificence. The great pediment, designed by the Duchess and carved by William Collins survives, pieced together and standing in the hen-run. The Duchess also designed Castle Farm, an enchanting Gothick farmhouse in the park, an eye catcher for the great house. (Worksop Manor is private, and not open to the public.) One more building of note remains to be mentioned: *Manor Lodge*, which might be glimpsed when driving along the A60 out of the town on a day in early spring, caught in strong sunshine through the bare trees, an immense house of unusual proportions standing to the N across ploughed fields, built apparently as a hunting lodge for Worksop Manor. If (with the owner's permission) it is approached close to, it will appear even more tremendous and enigmatic: above the ground floor two long side wings comprise four floors of low mullioned windows, with the wide projecting centre occupied by the enormous windows of two great rooms which each take up two full storeys—a Great Hall, and a Great Chamber above that: these were the great reception rooms, with the small rooms on either side bedrooms or retiring rooms. To add to all this there was once a sixth floor—a long gallery no doubt—with a flat roof above from which to watch the chase. It is a puzzling house, of prodigious size for a hunting lodge. The ground floor would have contained the offices and kitchens, with the front door up a flight of steps to the great hall on

the *piano nobile*. Architecturally it is connected with Shireoaks, Bolsover, Hardwick and Worksop: it was built almost certainly by Robert Smythson for Lord Shrewsbury; its panache proclaims his hand. For two centuries or more it was used as a farmhouse; its rescue and restoration in recent years are in no small measure due to its present owner. It stands here, mysterious, immensely impressive and, with its many blocked windows, seemingly withdrawn from the world—for all the proximity of collieries and industry.

Wysall [14] Undulating, pretty country close to the Leicestershire border: wide views across to Charnwood Forest. A village of good brick cottages, and two fine-looking 17th-century farmhouses. The *Church* stands prominent at the corner of the street: a clerestoried nave with a flat roof, a high pitched roof to the chancel, a tall embattled tower with a plain recessed spire. Inside, a venerable Norman N wall, a 13th-century tower arch, a 14th-century chancel, and an early 15th-century S arcade. And notable furnishings, too: the 15th-century screen survives, with stalls and misericords attached; the 15th-century pulpit, and (most rare) the tester or canopy for the altar, in the ancient timbered roof; there is a quaint tower ladder, perhaps as old as the tower itself. In the sanctuary is the tomb to Hugh Armstrong (1572) and his wife, Mary Sacheverell, with resplendent alabaster effigies; close to the pulpit is an unusual, painted wooden memorial to George Widmerpool (1689). An altogether rewarding country church.

A note on Nottinghamshire pronunciation

'They can't pronounce a "v" in Nottinghamshire,' it has been said: so Averham is Aram, Screveton is Screeton and Wiverton is Werton; Blidworth is Blid'th and Rainworth, Ran'rth. The old pronunciation of Worksop is Worsop. These may fox the outsider.

Index

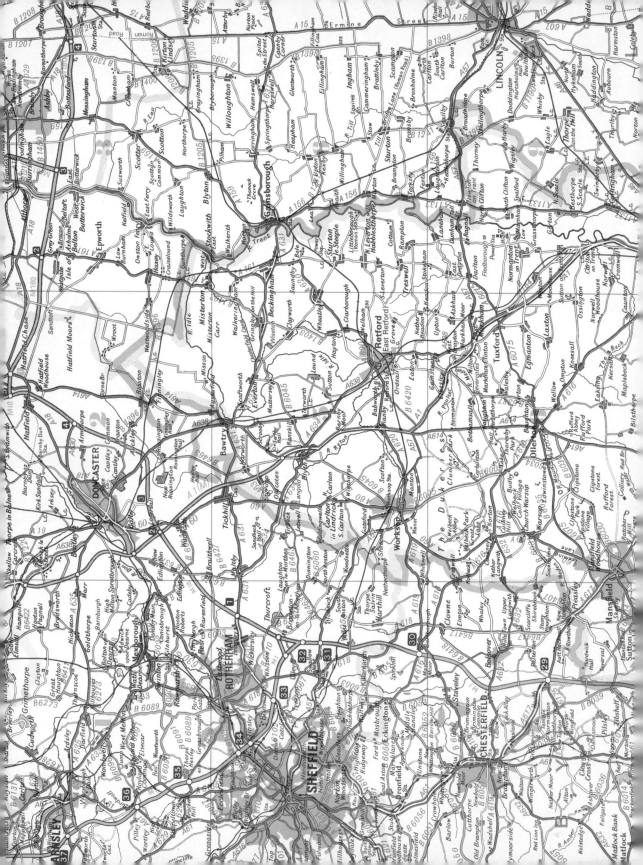

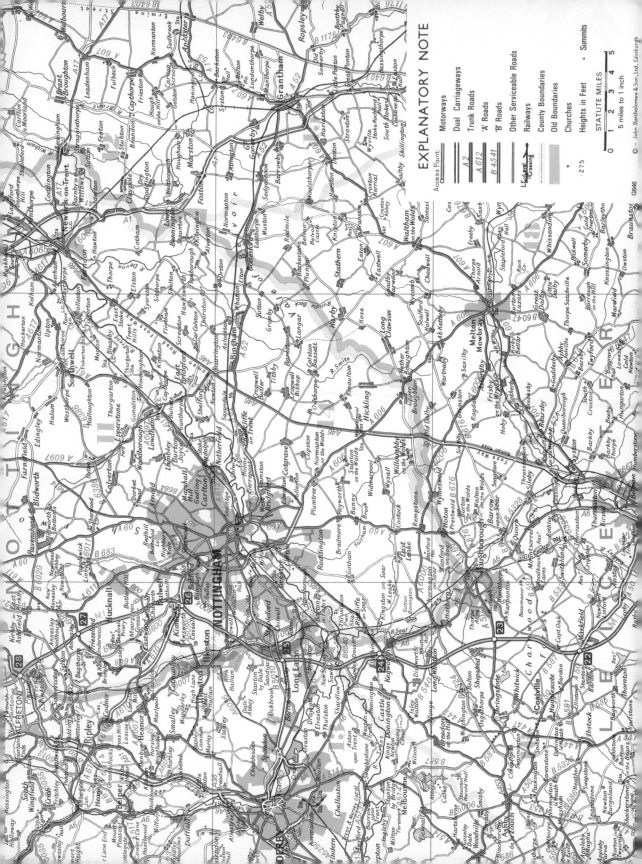

EXPLANATORY NOTE

Access Point:

Motorways

Dual Carriageways

Trunk Roads

'A' Roads — A 2

'A' Roads — A 612

'B' Roads — B 4541

Other Serviceable Roads

Railways

County Boundaries

Old Boundaries

Churches — +

Heights in Feet — ·275

Summits — ▲

Level Crossing

STATUTE MILES

0 1 2 3 4 5

5 miles to 1 inch

G646